DR. STEPHEN L. SNOVER, an Assistant Professor of Mathematics and Computer Science at the University of Hartford in Connecticut, was an author for the Boston University Mathematics Project, and has written articles on topics in both mathematics and computer science.

DR. MARK A. SPIKELL, a mathematics educator who is currently Chairman of the Department of Education at George Mason University in Fairfax, Virginia, has co-authored the books *Problem Solving in the Mathematics Laboratory* and *Multibase Activities*.

Jointly Professors Snover and Spikell are also co-authors of *How to Program Your Programmable Calculator*, a Spectrum book.

DR. STEPHEN L. SNOVER
DR. MARK SPIKELL

BRAIN
TICKLERS
PUZZLES & PASTIMES FOR
PROGRAMMABLE
CALCULATORS

A SPECTRUM BOOK

PRENTICE-HALL INC., Englewood Cliffs, New Jersey 07632

Library of Congress Cataloging in Publication Data

Snover, Stephen L
  Brian ticklers.

  (A Spectrum Book)
  1. Games—Data processing. 2. Games—Computer
programs. 3. Microcomputers—Programming.
I. Spikell, Mark A., joint author. II. Title.
GV1469.2.S64   794   80-22944
ISBN 0–13–081018–5
ISBN 0–13–081000–2 (pbk.)

Design by Dawn Stanley
Manufacturing supervision by Barbara Frick
Production coordination by Fred Dahl

A SPECTRUM BOOK

Printed in the United States of America

10 9 8 7 6 5 4 3 2 1

Prentice-Hall International, Inc., London
Prentice-Hall of Australia Pty. Limited, Sydney
Prentice-Hall of Canada, Ltd., Toronto
Prentice-Hall of India Private Limited, New Delhi
Prentice-Hall of Japan, Inc., Tokyo
Prentice-Hall of Southeast Asia Pte. Ltd., Singapore
Whitehall Books Limited, Wellington, New Zealand

CONTENTS

Contents

PREFACE

Now that personal computers and programmable calculators are so readily available, all of us should be aware of what we can do with them. What purposes can they be put to? What kinds of problems can they solve?

This collection of puzzles and pastimes is a resource of mathematical activities and recreations that can be solved conveniently on personal computers and programmable calculators. You need very little, if any, mathematical background in order to tackle these problems, because the calculator or computer can do the work for you.

WHO IS THE BOOK FOR?

It is probably for you. Anyone who wants to know the kinds of problems that can be solved on a personal computer and programmable calculator, as well as anyone who just wants to enjoy playing around with such a machine, will benefit from exploring these puzzles and pastimes. Specifically, this book makes an ideal gift or resource for . . .

- a computer hobbyist,
- a mathematics or science student,
- a programmable calculator owner,
- a personal computer owner,
- a computer science or mathematics teacher, or
- a science or mathematics enthusiast . . .

because the puzzles and pastimes

- form a collection of interesting, fun, and often challenging recreations,
- extend the range of problem-solving applications for programmable calculators and personal computers,
- stimulate the use of logical thinking and deductive reasoning, and
- provide a unique resource of problems—specifically chosen for solution with programmable calculators and personal or small computers.

IS A STRONG MATHEMATICAL
BACKGROUND NEEDED?

You need no more of a background than *high school algebra* to solve these puzzles and pastimes.

- Many of the problems require no more mathematics than is customarily taught in junior high school.
- Some of the problems involve mathematics from high school algebra and probability.
- For each problem, the relevant mathematics is developed and presented on the comment page accompanying the statement or the problem.

IS A LOT OF PROGRAMMING
EXPERIENCE NECESSARY?

If you have *some experience* with programming a programmable calculator or computer, that's helpful, since you must write and run programs to solve the problems. Extensive experience, however, is unnecessary.

- For those who desire such information, a set of hints and comments, accompanying each puzzle and pastime, describes a program to solve the problem.
- In the "Introduction," a detailed example is given explaining how to use the hints and comments in writing a program. Machine language programs are developed for the example for the TI 58 and TI 59 and HP33E programmable calculators and for BASIC and FORTRAN computer languages.
- Specific numerical answers are given for all the puzzles and pastimes, so you can check the accuracy of your program, no matter which language or machine you choose to use.
- BASIC programs are given for all the puzzles and pastimes in an appendix, since BASIC is one of the most widely used languages. In this way, interested persons

with appropriate machines may solve the problems by entering and running the programs without having to create them.

WHICH COMPUTER OR PROGRAMMABLE CALCULATOR DO I NEED?

Any computer or calculator that can be programmed is effective in solving these puzzles and pastimes, since this book is written to be independent of particular machines.

- Any computer can be used to solve all these problems.
- Almost any programmable calculator has enough program memory and programming features to solve all the problems in this collection. Your calculator will suffice as long as it has at least 50 program memory steps, several decision-making features (like: Is $x \geq 0$? Is $x = y$? or Is $x < t$?), and at least eight storage memory locations.

ACKNOWLEDGMENTS

We authors wish to thank several people for their positive influence in the creation and preparation of this book. First, thanks go to Judith Campbell for conceptualizing much of the artwork. Thanks also go to Mona Mark who prepared the finished artwork. Next we would like to recognize Anna Russak who helped testing out the validity and clarity of the problem statements by solving them on computer. Finally, special thanks go to Laurie and J. B. for their continual, good natured support.

Stephen L. Snover
Hartford CT 06105
Mark A. Spikell
Fairfax VA 22032

INTRODUCTION

This book presents a collection of puzzles and pastimes specifically chosen for personal computers and programmable calculators. Some of the problems are old, some are new. All have the unique features that they are too complicated or time-consuming to solve by hand but are readily done with the aid of a programmable calculating device. Because program solutions for each of the problems require a limited amount of memory, any of the problem-solving programs is small enough to fit the memory space in almost every currently available programmable calculator and certainly every personal computer. Hence, this special collection provides a unique resource of puzzles and pastimes that can all be done ideally on personal computers or programmable calculators.

Exploring puzzles and pastimes is a recreational activity that can provide you with many hours of relaxation and enjoyment. But more than that, you can learn a great deal from this exploration. We have chosen and arranged this collection in order to provide you with worthwhile learning experiences as well as entertainment based on our philosophy that you learn a lot by doing. Hopefully the original context of each puzzle and pastime will motivate you to want to try it. Then the Hints and Comments will give you the additional ideas on how to get started, where to go when stuck, and how to use elementary mathematics to advantage. As a byproduct of enjoying the process of problem solving, we know you will learn more programming skills like reading problem solving algorithms and translating them into your computer or calculator's own language. By exploring the problems, you will learn more about the capabilities of your machine and how to use it, along with elementary mathematical concepts to solve problems. Moreover you will have ample opportunity to reinforce what you have learned by solving the extensions accompanying each of the puzzles and pastimes. In short, we have designed this collection so that you can learn by doing while you are having fun.

FORMAT OF THE BOOK

The puzzles and pastimes are presented in an interesting context, for aesthetic appeal, and in a six-page format, for maximum functional appeal. As shown in Figures 1 and 2, the statement of the problem always appears on an odd-numbered (right-hand) page. Hearty problem solvers may tackle the writing of a program to solve the problem without using the additional information presented in the Hints and Comments, which follow on the next two pages.

The *Hints* are our specially designed method of supplying you with one step-by-step procedure from which you can write a program to solve the problem. Importantly, the Hints give both written and visual instructions on how our program is designed. The symbols, words, sentences, and the like to the right of the numbered steps are the written instructions for our program. The arrows connecting the numbered steps show the "flow" of the instructions and provide a "picture" of what is happening in the program as it solves the problem.

The *Comments* provide additional clarifying remarks. These remarks explain the purposes of various steps in the Hints or appropriate mathematical commentary, which may be of interest or useful in writing a program from our Hints.

The Hints and Comments are presented in separate sections for an important reason. We want you to use the Hints and Comments in whichever way suits you best. Some will choose to ignore the Hints and Comments altogether, preferring to develop completely their own program to solve the problem. Others will consult the Hints, Comments, or both merely to gain insight on a general approach in writing a program. Still others will find the Hints and Comments most useful as a step-by-step guide for writing a program to solve the problem.

In any case, if you decide to use the Hints and Comments, we know you will appreciate the machine-independent manner in which they are presented. It doesn't matter which programmable calculator or personal computer you use, the Hints—if carefully followed—will enable you to write a program for your machine's language.

As shown in Figure 3, the fifth page for each problem gives the numerical answer to the problem, along with a sample printout in

Figure 1

Figure 2

Figure 3

BASIC, so you can check to see whether the program you have written is accurate. We include these programs because BASIC is the most widely used language with personal computers, and some readers may wish to run programs rather than write them. These BASIC programs are easily adapted to obtain answers to the questions posed in the Extensions, which you will find on the next page. Extensions are presented so you can see how you can get more out of your programs than the solution of the original problem. Using answers to the questions posed in the Extensions are obtained by making some minor modification in your program.

In addition to the six-page format for each problem, an appendix includes the answers to the Extensions for each problem.

A SAMPLE PROBLEM—SAL'S VASES

The next few pages present a sample problem in the standard format already described. In the section following the sample problem, we show how to read and use the Hints and Comments to write a program that solves the problem of Sal's Vases. By working through this single example, you can see how to translate the Hints and Comments for any problem into a program.

SAL'S VASES

PROBLEM STATEMENTS

Some time ago, Sal bought 100 vases, which he has been selling at a flea market. After selling some over a few weeks, last week he had the remaining ones arranged neatly in 6 rows, with the same number of vases in each row. He sold 8 vases that week. This week, he has the remaining vases again arranged neatly in 11 rows, each row having just as many vases as each other row.

How many vases does Sal still have for sale?

HINTS

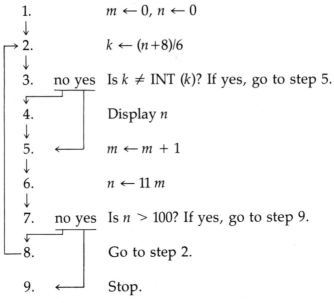

1. $m \leftarrow 0, n \leftarrow 0$

2. $k \leftarrow (n+8)/6$

3. no yes Is $k \neq$ INT (k)? If yes, go to step 5.

4. Display n

5. $m \leftarrow m + 1$

6. $n \leftarrow 11\, m$

7. no yes Is $n > 100$? If yes, go to step 9.

8. Go to step 2.

9. Stop.

n = number of vases
k = number of vases in each row last week
m = number of vases in each row this week

COMMENTS

Since the number n of vases Sal has now is a multiple of 11, there is some integer m so that

$$n = 11m \quad (1)$$

Furthermore, since n is 8 fewer than a multiple of 6, there is some integer k so that

$$n = 6k - 8 \quad (2)$$

Solving (2) for k gives the computational formula for k used in step 2 of the hints, namely:

$$k = (n + 8)/6$$

The loop between steps 2 and 8 of the hints makes sure that the number m of vases in each row this week is an integer by starting m at 0 and increasing m by 1 each time through the loop. In steps 1 and 6, n is obtained so that equation (1) holds. Then, in step 2, k is computed so that equation 2 holds. While m is always an integer, k is not. If "Is $k \neq$ INT (k)?" has a "no" answer (Step 3), k is indeed an integer and a possible number for Sal's number of vases has been found. If this is the case, n is displayed in Step 4. If k is not an integer, step 4 is skipped. When $n > 100$ (Step 7) the looping concludes, since all values of n less than or equal to 100 have been considered.

ANSWERS AND EXTENSIONS

ANSWERS: Sal could have either 22 or 88 vases left to sell. The information given in the problem is not enough to distinguish between these two values.

```
0005 REM SALS VASES
0010 LET M=0
0015 LET N=0
0020 LET K=(N+8)/6
0030 IF K<>INT(K) THEN GOTO 0050
0040 PRINT N
0050 LET M=M+1
0060 LET N=11*M
0070 IF N>100 THEN GOTO 0090
0080 GOTO 0020
0090 END
```

EXTENSIONS:
(Answers to the extensions of Sal's Vases will be found in Appendix I.)

   i. How many vases could Sal have if he had sold 5 vases between last week and this? To answer this, change step 2 of the problem to become:

$$2. \ k \leftarrow (n+ 5)/6$$

  ii. Suppose Sal started long ago with 200 vases, had (fewer) vases arranged last week in 8 rows, and after selling 6 vases had the rest arranged this week in 7 rows. How many vases could he have now? Change steps 2, 6, and 7 to accomplish this:

      2. $k \leftarrow (n + 6)/8$
      6. $n \leftarrow 7m$
      7. Is $n > 200$? If yes, go to step 9.

READING AND USING
HINTS AND COMMENTS

You can use the Hints presented with any problem in several ways. For example, they can be used as a stylistic guide to writing programs that solve the problems. If you choose to use the Hints in this way, you might want to know why they actually lead to a program that solves the problem. The Comments associated with the Hints are designed to provide this information for you. While it is often not necessary to consult the Comments, they may be useful for certain interested readers.

Another way to use the Hints is as a step-by-step procedure for designing a program to solve the problem on your particular machine. To do so, you need to understand what the symbols and other notations in the Hints mean. In this section we describe in detail the Hints given for the problem of Sal's Vases. This illustrates for you just how our Hints can be read and translated into a program for your machine. Furthermore, we provide at the end of this introduction a glossary of symbols, functions, and decision tests used in our Hints for the various problems. The Glossary gives additional information that helps you to read and use the Hints.

Each number below corresponds to the step number in the Hints section for the problem of Sal's Vases.

1. The letters m and n represent the number of vases in each row this week and the total number of vases, respectively. In general, each different letter used identifies a quantity to be stored in some memory location. The symbol $\leftarrow$ means "is replaced by." Hence, the instructions in this step
$$m \leftarrow 0, \quad n \leftarrow 0$$
mean "place zero in the locations reserved for m and n."
2. The letter k represents the number of vases in each row last week. Hence, the instruction in this step says to compute $(n + 8)/6$ and place the result in the location reserved for k.

3. This conditional test determines whether or not the current value of k is an integer. See the glossary in section 5 of this introduction for an explanation of the INT function. If k is not an integer, the program branches to step 5. If k is an integer, the program continues to step 4.

4. Here, the program displays or prints the current value of n.

5. In this step, the value of m is increased by one and the new quantity replaces the previous value stored in the memory location reserved for m.

6. In this step, the quantity $11m$ (eleven times m) is computed and replaces the existing value stored in the memory location reserved for n.

7. This conditional test determines whether or not n is greater than 100. If it is, the program branches to step 9. If it is not, then the program continues to step 8.

8. Here the program loops back to step 2 and continues.

9. At this step, the program stops having displayed or printed all possible solutions to the problem.

For the problem of Sal's Vases you might want to note the general way in which the Comments can (but need not) be useful in understanding the Hints.

The first part of the Comments shows the elementary algebra that leads to the conclusion that the number of vases, k, in each row last week is given by the formula

$$k = (n + 8)/6$$

This formula becomes step 2 of the Hints. Thus, even if you are not able to develop the formula on your own, we show you how it was obtained in the Comments.

The second part of the Comments shows how the Hints are organized using the programming features of looping and decision making. It also explains why this organization leads to a program that solves the problem.

Thus the Hints and Comments provide a great deal of flexibility in helping you to create programs that solve the problems in this book.

WRITING PROGRAMS FROM
THE HINTS

Since the Hints are always made up of a handful of fundamental statements, you should be aware of these kinds of statements and know how to translate them into your calculator or computer's language. From the Hints accompanying Sal's Vases, all the fundamental statements we use in the Hints in this book can be illustrated by example. (See chart on next page.) So that you can see examples of how actual programs are prepared, we provide programs for the solution of the problem of Sal's Vases for the TI 58, TI 59 and HP 33E programmable calculators and for BASIC and FORTRAN computer languages. These programs, on the final pages of this introduction, have been written directly from the Hints given for the problem of Sal's vases. Examine and run the appropriate program corresponding to the language of your machine.

For your convenience, the nine single-digit numbers to the left of the program steps correspond to the nine lines of the hints for the problem of Sal's Vases.

STEPS IN SAL'S VASES HINTS	DESCRIPTION OF FUNDAMENTAL STATEMENT	FEATURES USED WITH:			
		TI 58 and TI 59	HP33E	BASIC	FORTRAN
1.	input of values	STO	STO	LET statement	Assignment statement
2.	computation of values	$+$, $-$, $\times$, $\div$, RCL, etc. in x-register	$+$, $-$, $\times$, $\div$, RCL, etc. in x-register	LET statement	Assignment statement
3. & 7.	conditional branch	2nd $x = t$, INV 2nd $x = t$, 2nd $x \geqslant t$, INV 2nd $x \geqslant t$	$fx > y$, $fx = y$, $gx < 0$, $gx = 0$, etc.	IF . . . THEN . . . or IF . . . THEN GO TO	IF statement
4.	output of values	RCL and R/S	RCL and R/S	PRINT	WRITE and FORMAT or PRINT
5. & 6.	update of values	SUM, 2nd PRD memory arithmetic or x-reg. comp.	STO $+ n$, STO $\times n$ memory arith. or x-reg. comp.	LET statement	Assignment statement
8.	unconditional branch	GTO n	GTO nn	GO TO	GO TO
9.	end program	R/S	R/S	STOP, END	STOP, END

TI 58 AND TI 59

1. 000 0
   001 STO
   002 01
   003 STO
   004 02

2. 005 2nd Lbl
   006 A
   007 RCL
   008 01
   009 +
   010 8
   011 =
   012 ÷
   013 6
   014 =

3. 015 STO
   016 03
   017 $x \gtrless t$

   018 RCL
   019 03
   020 2nd Int
   021 INV
   022 2nd $x = t$
   023 B

4. 024 RCL
   025 01
   026 R/S

5. 027 2nd Lbl
   028 B
   029 1
   030 SUM
   031 02

6. 032 RCL
   033 02
   034 ×

   035 1
   036 1
   037 =
   038 STO
   039 01

7. 040 RCL
   041 04
   042 $x \gtrless t$
   043 RCL
   044 01
   045 2nd $x \geqslant t$

8. 046 C
   047 A

9. 048 2nd Lbl
   049 C
   050 R/S

memory usage: $R_{01} = n$, $R_{02} = m$, $R_{03} = k$, $R_{04} = 101$, t-register
= k.

initialization: 101, STO 04, RST, R/S

HP 33E

1. 00 (R/S)
   01 0
   02 STO 1
   03 STO 2

2. 04 RCL 1
   05 8
   06 +
   07 6
   08 ÷

3. 09 ENTER ↑
   10 g INT
   11 $f x \neq y$
   12 GTO 15

4. 13 RCL 1
   14 R/S

5. 15 1
   16 STO + 2

6. 17 RCL 2
   18 1
   19 1
   20 ×
   21 STO 1

7. 22 RCL 4
   23 RCL 1
   24 $f x \leqslant y$

8. 25 GTO 00

9. 26 GTO 04

memory usage: $R_1 = n$, $R_2 = m$, $R_4 = 100$
initialization: 100, STO 4, R/S

```
                    BASIC

          5   REM SAL'S VASES
1.    1Ø    LET M = Ø
      15    LET N = Ø
2.    2Ø    LET K = (N + 8)/6
3.    3Ø    IF K < > INT (K) THEN 5Ø
4.    4Ø    PRINT N
5.    5Ø    LET M = M + 1
6.    6Ø    LET N = 11 * M
7.    7Ø    IF N > 1ØØ THEN 9Ø
8.    8Ø    GO TO 2Ø
9.    9Ø    END
```

FORTRAN

	Columns: 1 2 3 4 5	6	7
	C		SAL'S VASES
			INTEGER M, N
			REAL K
1.			M = Ø
			N = Ø
2.	2		K = (N + 8.)/6.
3.			IF (K .NE. AINT (K)) GO TO 5
4.			WRITE (6, 1ØØ) N
	1 Ø Ø		FORMAT (Ø14)
5.	5		M = M + 1
6.			N = 11 * M
7.			IF (N .GT. 1ØØ) STOP
8.			GO TO 2
9.			END

GLOSSARY OF GENERAL SYMBOLS, FUNCTIONS, AND DECISION TESTS

SYMBOL OR NAME	MEANING
$a, b, c, \ldots$ any lower case alphabet letter	symbols for storage memory locations
$\leftarrow$	"is replaced by" symbol; for example, $a \leftarrow b + 1$ means storage memory location a is replaced by one more than the value in storage memory location b.
3. $\downarrow$ 4.	symbols for normal "flow" of program steps; used between consecu-tive steps of the hints
↑_3.	unconditional branching symbol, used to indicate a loop in the hints
3. no yes ↓ 4. ↓	conditional branching symbol, used to indicate a decision test in the hints

SYMBOL OR NAME	MEANING
INT (X)	integer part of X function; obtains the greatest integer less than or equal to X.
FRAC (X)	fractional part of X function; obtains the non-integer part of X as $$\text{FRAC }(X) = X - \text{INT}(X)$$
ABS(X)	absolute value of X function; obtains the size of X by taking the value of X and making its sign positive.
log (X)	the base 10 logarithm of X
round-off function	use INT$(X + .5)$ to find the nearest whole number to X
random number generator	use FRAC (143X) or FRAC $[(X + \pi)^5]$ to find a "random" decimal number between 0 and 1
number of digits counter	use INT $[\log (X)] + 1$ to obtain the number of digits in X
digit extractor	use 10[FRAC (X/10)] or more appropriately INT [10(FRAC (X/10)) + .5] which is more accurate on some calculators and computers. This obtains the right-most digit of the integer X.
Integer tests	use Is X = INT (X)? or Is X ≠ INT (X)? or equivalently use Is FRAC (X) = 0? or Is FRAC (X) ≠ 0? to test whether X is an integer or not.
Perfect square tests	use Is $\sqrt{X}$ = INT $(\sqrt{X})$? or Is $\sqrt{X}$ ≠ INT $(\sqrt{X})$? or for more accurate results on some machines, first compute R ← INT $(\sqrt{X} + .5)$ then use Is (R) (R) = X? or Is (R) (R) = X? to test whether X is a perfect square or not

PROBLEM DIFFICULTY CHART

Problems in this collection are arbitrarily arranged. Readers interested in some idea of the level of difficulty for particular problems may find the chart on this page useful. It is merely a guide based on the authors' judgment. There are three categories—easy, medium, and hard.

BRAIN
TICKLERS

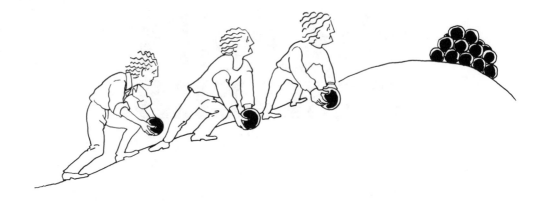

THE PYRAMID
OF CANNONBALLS

PROBLEM STATEMENT

From a collection of 10,000 cannonballs, a square-based pyramid is built with a single cannonball on top and a square number on each layer. How many layers can be made? And how many cannonballs will be left over?

HINTS

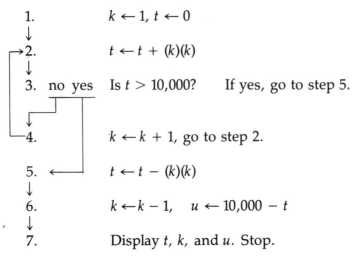

1. $k \leftarrow 1, t \leftarrow 0$

2. $t \leftarrow t + (k)(k)$

3. no yes Is $t > 10,000$? If yes, go to step 5.

4. $k \leftarrow k + 1$, go to step 2.

5. $t \leftarrow t - (k)(k)$

6. $k \leftarrow k - 1, \quad u \leftarrow 10,000 - t$

7. Display t, k, and u. Stop.

k = the number of layers
t = total number of cannon balls in k layers
u = the number of unused cannonballs

COMMENTS

The purpose of the loop between steps 2 and 4 is to total up the number of cannonballs needed to build the top k layers of the pyramid. Step 2 adds the number, k^2, of cannonballs in the kth layer (counting from the top down) to a running total of cannonballs. Each time through the loop, k is increased by 1 so that consecutive layers are considered. The first time the question ("Is $t > 10,000$?") obtains a "yes" answer, too many cannonballs have been added to the total for the first time. Therefore step 5 "peels off" the number of cannonballs in the largest layer, and step 6 reduces the count of layers, k, by one. In this way the largest square-based pyramid is found that can be formed with no more than 10,000 cannonballs.

ANSWERS AND EXTENSIONS

ANSWERS: A pyramid of 30 layers can be made using all but 545 of the 10,000 cannonballs.

```
0005 REM PYRAMID OF CANNONBALLS
0010 LET K=1
0015 LET T=0
0020 LET T=T+K*K
0030 IF T>10000 THEN GOTO 0050
0040 LET K=K+1
0045 GOTO 0020
0050 LET T=T-K*K
0060 LET K=K-1
0065 LET U=10000-T
0070 PRINT "NUMBER OF LAYERS IS ";K
0073 PRINT "NUMBER OF CANNONBALLS USED IS ";T
0077 PRINT "NUMBER OF UNUSED CANNONBALLS IS ";U
0080 END
```

EXTENSIONS:

i. How many cannonballs are required to build a square-based pyramid with 50 layers?
   This question can be answered with the aid of the Hints, if step 3 is changed to:

   3. Is $k = 50$?   If yes, go to step 7.

ii. There is only one square-based pyramid containing, in total, a square number of cannonballs (other than the trivial case of a pyramid made from a single cannonball). Can you find it? Change steps 1 and 3 of the hints and add step 3.5 as follows in order to locate the number:

   1. $k \leftarrow 2, t \leftarrow 1$
   3. $r \leftarrow \text{INT} (\sqrt{t} + .5)$
   3.5 Is $t = (r)(r)$? If yes, got to step 7.

iii. Suppose instead of totaling squares, you total cubes. When is the sum of the first k cubes a perfect square? To answer this, change steps 2 and 3 and add step 3.5 to:

   2. $t \leftarrow t + (k)(k)(k)$
   3. $r \leftarrow \text{INT} (\sqrt{t} + .5)$
   3.5 Is t $= (r)(r)$? If yes, got to step 7.

THE NARCISSISTIC
CUBES

PROBLEM STATEMENT

Narcissistic cubes are positive integers that exactly equal the sum of the cubes of their digits. Thus, 370 and 371 are both narcissistic cubes since

$$370 = 3^3 + 7^3 + 0^3$$

$$371 = 3^3 + 7^3 + 1^3$$

However, $483 \neq 4^3 + 8^3 + 3^3$.

Excluding the trivial case of 1, only two other narcissistic cubes exist. What are all four narcissistic cubes?

HINTS

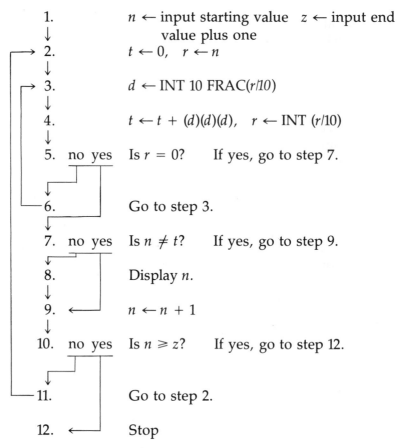

1. $n \leftarrow$ input starting value $z \leftarrow$ input end
              value plus one

2. $t \leftarrow 0, \quad r \leftarrow n$

3. $d \leftarrow$ INT 10 FRAC($r/10$)

4. $t \leftarrow t + (d)(d)(d), \quad r \leftarrow$ INT ($r/10$)

5. no yes   Is $r = 0$?   If yes, go to step 7.

6.   Go to step 3.

7. no yes   Is $n \neq t$?   If yes, go to step 9.

8.   Display n.

9. ← $n \leftarrow n + 1$

10. no yes   Is $n \geqslant z$?   If yes, go to step 12.

11.   Go to step 2.

12. ←   Stop

n = starting value of the number to be checked
z = ending value plus one
t = total of cubes and digits
r = remaining part of n after digits have been removed
d = current digit removed from n

COMMENTS

In order to locate narcissistic cubes, the hints are designed with two loops. The inner loop, between steps 3 and 6, has the purpose of picking off the digits of an integer, n, one by one (step 3), cubing each digit, and totaling these cubes (step 4).

The test "Is $r = 0$?" decides whether or not more digits of n need to be picked off, cubed, and added to the total of cubes of digits. When all the digits have been removed—that is, when $r = 0$—then t is the total of cubes of digits, and t can then be compared to n. If the result of the test "Is $n \neq t$?" is "yes," n is not a narcissistic cube and is not displayed. Otherwise, n is narcissistic and is displayed in step 8.

The outer loop, steps 2 through 11, has the effect of checking all integer values of n between an initial value and an ending value chosen in step 1. As such, the outer loop locates and displays all narcissistic cubes between these two chosen values.

ANSWERS AND EXTENSIONS

ANSWERS: All the narcissistic cubes that are positive integers
are 1, 153, 370, 371, and 407.

```
0005 REM NARCISSISTIC CUBES
0010 PRINT "WHAT IS THE FIRST N VALUE";
0011 INPUT N
0015 PRINT "WHAT IS ONE MORE THAN THE LAST N VALUE";
0016 INPUT Z
0018 PRINT
0019 PRINT
0020 LET T=0
0025 LET R=N
0030 LET D=INT(10*(R/10-INT(R/10))+.5)
0040 LET T=T+D*D*D
0045 LET R=INT(R/10)
0050 IF R=0 THEN GOTO 0070
0060 GOTO 0030
0070 IF N<>T THEN GOTO 0090
0080 PRINT "NARCISSISTIC CUBE IS ";N
0090 LET N=N+1
0100 IF N>=Z THEN GOTO 0120
0110 GOTO 0020
0120 END
```

EXTENSIONS:

i. Using the Hint given, you can find positive integers that equal the sums of the squares of their digits, sums of fourth powers of their digits, and so on. Merely change step 4 of the hints to:

4. $t \leftarrow t + d^a$, $r \leftarrow$ INT $(r/10)$

where a is the desired power. For example, to find the positive integers that euqal the sums of the squares of their digits, change step 4 to:

4. $t \leftarrow t + d^2$, $r \leftarrow$ INT $(r/10)$

ii. Notice that $1233 = 12^2 + 33^2$. Are there any other four-digit integers with this property? To explore the problem, change the Hints as follows:

1. $n \leftarrow 1000$, $z \leftarrow 9999$
3. $d \leftarrow$ INT$(100($FRAC$(r/100)) + .5)$
4. $t \leftarrow t + d^2$, $r \leftarrow$ INT $(r/100)$

THE PRISONERS' DILEMMA

PROBLEM STATEMENT

In the country of Ambivola, the prisons are too crowded. So the magistrate decides to offer each prisoner the unusual opportunity to determine by luck whether he may go free or must remain in the prison. Each prisoner is to be given 10 green and 10 red marbles along with two urns. He must place all the marbles into the urns, but he can arrange them any way he likes, as long as each urn has at least one marble. Then, when blindfolded, he must choose one of the two urns and then choose one of the marbles in that urn. If he chooses a green marble, he can go free but by choosing a red one, he must remain in prison, How should a prisoner arrange the marbles in the two urns in order to maximize his chances of going free?

HINTS

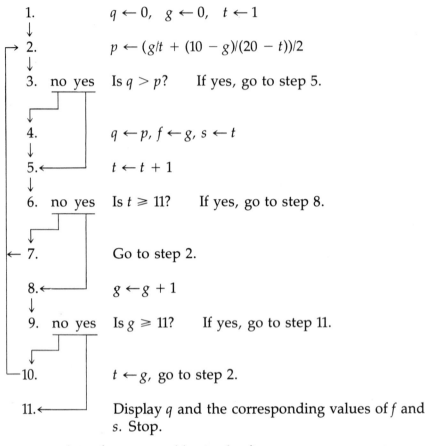

1. $q \leftarrow 0, \quad g \leftarrow 0, \quad t \leftarrow 1$

2. $p \leftarrow (g/t + (10 - g)/(20 - t))/2$

3.   no yes   Is $q > p$?   If yes, go to step 5.

4. $q \leftarrow p, f \leftarrow g, s \leftarrow t$

5. $t \leftarrow t + 1$

6.   no yes   Is $t \geqslant 11$?   If yes, go to step 8.

7.   Go to step 2.

8. $g \leftarrow g + 1$

9.   no yes   Is $g \geqslant 11$?   If yes, go to step 11.

10. $t \leftarrow g$, go to step 2.

11.   Display q and the corresponding values of f and s. Stop.

g = number of green marbles in the first urn
t = total number of green and red marbles in the first urn
p = probability corresponding to values of g and t
q = maximum probability
f = number of green marbles in the first urn for maximum probability
s = total number of marbles in the first urn for maximum probability

COMMENTS

The probability of choosing a green marble from one or the other of the urns is

$$\text{Prob (green)} = (g/t + (10 - g)/(20 - t))/2$$

as shown by the decision tree below where $g =$ the number of green marbles and $t =$ the total number of marbles in urn #1.

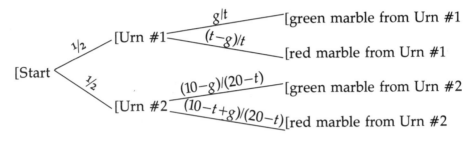

Since it does not matter which urn is called urn #1, let this urn be the one with 10 or fewer marbles in total. Then the numbers g and t must fall within the intervals:

$$0 \leqslant g \leqslant 10 \quad \text{and} \quad g \leqslant t \leqslant 10.$$

Since each urn must not be empty, it is also necessary that

$$t \neq 0$$

In step 2 of the Hints, the probability corresponding to each choice of g and t is computed. Steps 3 and 4 decide whether this probability p is larger than the previously calculated largest probability. If so, the new p, g, and t values are stored in q, f, and s, respectively.

The loop between steps 2 and 7 creates all the required choices of t corresponding to a fixed g value. The loop between steps 2 and 10 creates the different g values. Together these loops produce all the possible combinations of g and t values for the ranges

$$0 \leqslant g \leqslant 10, \quad g \leqslant t \leqslant 10$$

(except for the combination with $g = t = 0$, because of step 1).

ANSWERS AND EXTENSIONS

ANSWER: A prisoner maximizes his probability of being set free by placing one green marble in one urn and all the other marbles in the other urn. In this case, the probability of being set free is 0.7368 or about 74%.

```
0005 REM PRISONERS DILEMMA
0010 LET U=0
0013 LET G=0
0017 LET T=1
0020 LET P=(G/T+(10-G)/(20-T))/2
0030 IF U>P THEN GOTO 0050
0040 LET U=P
0043 LET F=G
0047 LET S=T
0050 LET T=T+1
0060 IF T>=11 THEN GOTO 0080
0070 GOTO 0020
0080 LET G=G+1
0090 IF G>=11 THEN GOTO 0110
0100 LET T=G
0105 GOTO 0020
0110 PRINT "MAXIMUM PROBABILITY IS ";U
0115 PRINT "PRISONER SHOULD PLACE ";F;"GREEN MARBLES"
0114 PRINT "AND ";S-F;"RED MARBLES IN THE FIRST URN"
0115 PRINT "IN ORDER TO MAXIMIZE THE PROBABILITY OF"
0116 PRINT "BEING SET FREE"
0120 END
```

EXTENSIONS:

i. What happens if the prisoner is required to use 15 green and 15 red marbles? This question can be answered by changing the intervals for the possibilities of g and t as follows:

$$0 \leqslant g \leqslant 15 \quad \text{and} \quad g \leqslant t \leqslant 15 \quad (\text{with } t \geqslant 1)$$

Steps 2, 6, and 9 in the Hints need to be correspondingly changed to become:

2. $p \leftarrow (g/t + (15-g)/(30-t))/2$
6. Is $t \geqslant 16$?   If yes, go to step 8.
9. Is $g \geqslant 16$?   If yes, go to step 11.

ii. What happens if the prisoner is required to use 20 marbles of each color? 30 marbles of each color? And so on to 100 marbles of each color?
In a manner similar to extension (i), only steps 2, 6, and 9 of the Hints need to be adapted.

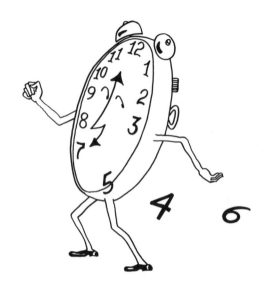

THE MALFUNCTIONING
CLOCK

PROBLEM STATEMENT

A clock loses a different amount of time each hour according to the following schedule?

HOUR	TIME LOST
1	1/2 minute
2	1/4 minute
3	2/8 minute
4	3/16 minute
5	5/32 minute
6	8/64 minute
7	13/128 minute
$\vdots$	$\cdot$
n	$f(n)/2^n$ minute

where $f(n)$ is the nth Fibonacci number; that is, $f(1) = 1, f(2) = 1,$
$f(3) = 2, f(4) = 3, f(5) = 5, f(6) = 8, f(7) = 13, \cdots$, and, in general,
$f(n) = f(n-1) + f(n-2)$ for all $n \geqslant 3$.

How much time does the clock lose in 24 hours?

HINTS

1. $d \leftarrow 1, \quad e \leftarrow 1, \quad f \leftarrow 0, \quad t \leftarrow 0, \quad h \leftarrow 0$

2. $h \leftarrow h + 1, \quad d \leftarrow 2d$

3. $g \leftarrow e + f$

4. $e \leftarrow f$

5. $f \leftarrow g$

6. $t \leftarrow t + g/d$

7. no yes Is $h = 24$? If yes, go to step 9.

8.   Go to step 2.

9. ←   Display t. Stop.

h = hour of the day
d = current denominator
e = second previous Fibonacci number
f = previous Fibonacci number
g = current Fibonacci number
t = running total of (lost) time

COMMENTS

The loop between steps 2 and 8 creates the total time lost as a running total of minutes lost during each of the 24 hours of the day.

In step 2 the next hour number and the next denominator are computed. Step 3 produces the next Fibonacci number using the formula:

$$f(n) = f(n-1) + f(n-2)$$

which in the Hints is stated as $g \leftarrow e + f$. Furthermore, steps 4 and 5 shift the two previous Fibonacci numbers so that the latest ones are saved. Step 6 then computes the fractional number of minutes, g/d, that the clock loses in the hth hour and adds this fraction into the running total, t.

If $h = 24$, that is, if 24 fractions have been totaled, the value of t is displayed. Otherwise, the loop is repeated from step 2.

ANSWERS AND EXTENSIONS

ANSWER: The clock loses 1.98829 minutes in 24 hours; that is, the clock loses almost 2 minutes.

```
0005 REM THE MALFUNCTIONING CLOCK
0010 LET D=1
0012 LET E=1
0014 LET F=0
0016 LET T=0
0018 LET H=0
0020 LET H=H+1
0025 LET D=2*D
0030 LET G=E+F
0040 LET E=F
0050 LET F=G
0060 LET T=T+G/D
0070 IF H=24 THEN GOTO 0090
0080 GOTO 0020
0090 PRINT "THE CLOCK LOSES ";T;" MINUTES IN ";H;" HOURS."
0100 END
```

EXTENSIONS:

i. How much time would be lost in 48 hours? In 72 hours?
    To answer these questions, change step 7 of the Hints to:

    7. Is $h = 48$? If yes, go to step 9.
                or
    7. Is $h = 72$? If yes, go to step 9.

ii. While the clock loses essentially 2 minutes in 3 days (72
    hours), not all of these 72 hours are needed to obtain a
    total time loss of 2 minutes—if the time loss is rounded-
    off to six significant digits. That means the time loss
    appears to be exactly 2 minutes for a certain hour, h,
    when the next fractional time lost is smaller than 5×10^{-7}.
    What is the first hour, h, for which the time lost appears
    to be exactly 2 minutes, when rounded off to six signifi-
    cant digits?

    Change steps 7 and 9 of the Hints as follows in order to
    investigate this question.

    7. Is $g/d < 5 \times 10^{-7}$? If yes, go to step 9.
    9. Display t and h.   Stop.

iii. How much time would the clock lose in 24 hours if the
    denominators were powers of 3 rather than powers of 2?
    To solve this, change step 2 to:

    2. $h \leftarrow h + 1, \quad d \leftarrow 3d$

THE EFFICIENCY EXPERT

PROBLEM STATEMENT

A manufacturer has two machines, a Glyxer and a Ploofer, capable of making television screens for color sets. In an effort to maximize the yearly production of screens, the manufacturer hires an efficiency expert to determine the number of days each machine should be in operation. In the report, the expert indicates that the maximum yearly production will occur when

$$440y + 279x = 169{,}780$$

for integer values of x and y, the number of full days the Glyxer and Ploofer should run, respectively.

How many days should the manufacturer operate each machine in order to maximize production?

HINTS

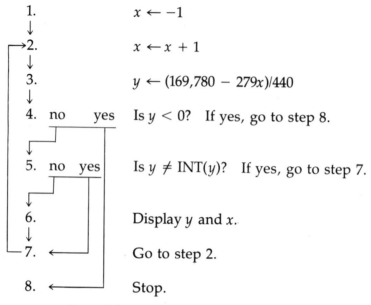

1. $x \leftarrow -1$

2. $x \leftarrow x + 1$

3. $y \leftarrow (169{,}780 - 279x)/440$

4.   no   yes   Is $y < 0$?   If yes, go to step 8.

5.   no   yes   Is $y \neq$ INT(y)?   If yes, go to step 7.

6.   Display y and x.

7. $\leftarrow$ Go to step 2.

8. $\leftarrow$ Stop.

x = number of days the Glyxer machine runs
y = number of days the Ploofer machine runs

COMMENTS

The problem is solved by finding integer values of x and y satisfying the equation $y = (169{,}780 - 279x)/440$, which is another form of $440y + 279x = 169{,}780$.

The loop between steps 2 and 7 computes a value of y for a specific value of x and checks whether y is a non-negative integer. Each time through the loop, x increases by 1 and y simultaneously decreases. Thus, when the test "Is $y < 0$?" obtains a "yes" answer, no more values of x and y need to be checked.

ANSWERS AND EXTENSIONS

ANSWERS: Maximum production occurs when the Glyxer machine operates 260 days and the Ploofer machine operates 221 days.

```
0005 REM THE EFFICIENCY EXPERT
0010 LET X=-1
0020 LET X=X+1
0030 LET Y=(169780-279*X)/440
0040 IF Y<0 THEN GOTO 0080
0050 IF Y<>INT(Y) THEN GOTO 0070
0060 PRINT "RUN GLYXER FOR ";X;" DAYS"
0065 PRINT "RUN PLOOFER FOR ";Y;" DAYS"
0070 GOTO 0020
0080 END
```

EXTENSIONS:

i. The Hint for this problem can be used to find integer values of x and y satisfying any equation of the form

$$ay + bx = c$$

which can be rewritten as

$$y = (c - bx)/a$$

and shows how to rewrite step 3 of the Hint. For example, changing step 3 to

3. $y \leftarrow (1{,}000 - 17x)/77$

enables you to obtain the unique solution $x = 9$, $y = 11$ to the equation $77y + 17x = 1{,}000$. Changing step 3 to

3. $y \leftarrow (123{,}456 - 233x)/220$

enables you to obtain the two sets of positive integers satisfying

$$220y + 233x = 123{,}456$$

What are the two sets of integers?

ii. Hearty problem-solvers may enjoy making up their own versions of the efficiency expert problem by finding appropriate values of a, b, and c that give a unique solution to

$$ay + bx = c.$$

PERVASIVE ROOTS

PROBLEM STATEMENT

a. $\sqrt{6 + \sqrt{6 + \sqrt{6 + \ldots}}}$ $= ?$

b. $\sqrt[3]{60 + \sqrt[3]{60 + \sqrt[3]{60 + \ldots}}}$ $= ?$

c. $\sqrt{7 - \sqrt{7 + \sqrt{7 - \ldots}}}$ $= ?$

HINTS

1. $r \leftarrow 2, \quad n \leftarrow 6$

2. $p \leftarrow 0$

3. $s \leftarrow (n + p)^{1/r}$

4.   no   yes   Is $s = p$?   If yes, go to step 6.

5. $p \leftarrow s$. Go to step 3.

6.   Display s. Stop

r = kind of root to be taken
n = number inside root symbols
p = previous value calculation
s = current value calculation

COMMENTS

The loop between steps 3 and 5 repeats a root calculation and has the effect of evaluating the pervasive roots from inside out. With $r=2$, $n=6$, and $p=0$, the first time through the loop s becomes (in step 3)

$$s = \sqrt{6+0} = \sqrt{6}$$

The second time through s is changed to

$$s = \sqrt{6+ \sqrt{6}}$$

The third time yields

$$s = \sqrt{6 + \sqrt{6 + \sqrt{6}}}$$

After the loop is repeated numerous times, the sequence of s values tends to a limit $s = \sqrt{6 + \sqrt{6 + \sqrt{6 + \sqrt{6 + \ldots}}}}$
This limit is the desired value of the pervasive root. The loop is designed to stop when two successive s values are equal.

To solve problem b, merely change step 1 in the Hints to read:

1. $r \leftarrow 3$, $n \leftarrow 60$

Similarly, to solve problem c, change steps 1 and 3 to read:

1. $r \leftarrow 2$, $n \leftarrow 7$
3. $s \leftarrow (n - (n+ p)^{1/r})^{1/r}$

ANSWERS AND EXTENSIONS

ANSWERS: The answers to problems a, b, and c are 3, 4, and 2, respectively.

a.

```
0005 REM PERVASIVE ROOTS
0010 LET R=2
0015 LET N=6
0020 LET P=0
0030 LET S=(N+P)^(1/R)
0040 IF S=P THEN GOTO 0060
0050 LET P=S
0055 GOTO 0030
0060 PRINT "PERVASIVE ROOT IS ";S
0070 END
```

b.

```
0005 REM PERVASIVE ROOTS
0010 LET R=3
0015 LET N=60
0020 LET P=0
0030 LET S=(N+P)^(1/R)
0040 IF S=P THEN GOTO 0060
0050 LET P=S
0055 GOTO 0030
0060 PRINT "PERVASIVE ROOT IS ";S
0070 END
```

c.

```
0005 REM PERVASIVE ROOTS
0010 LET R=2
0015 LET N=7
0020 LET P=0
0030 LET S=(N-(N+P)^(1/R))^(1/R)
0040 IF S=P THEN GOTO 0060
0050 LET P=S
0055 GOTO 0030
0060 PRINT "PERVASIVE ROOT IS ";S
0070 END
```

EXTENSIONS:

i. Which integer input values give integer results for problem a? In other words, for which values of n does the following pervasive root have an integer value?

$$\sqrt{n + \sqrt{n + \sqrt{n + \ldots}}}$$

To explore this question, use the Hint given for the original problem but test different values of n in step 1.

ii. What integer input values give integer results for the following pervasive root problem?

$$\sqrt[r]{n + \sqrt[r]{n + \sqrt[r]{n + \ldots}}}$$

To explore this question, use the Hint given for the original problem but test different values of r and n in step 1.

THE GAME OF 100

PROBLEM STATEMENT

Here is a game for two players, you and your machine. The first player, you, selects any number from 1 to 10. The second player, the machine, then selects any number from 1 to 10 and adds it to your number to obtain a running total, t.

The game continues with you and your machine alternately taking turns. During each turn, a number from 1 to 10 is selected and added to the running total.

The player who makes the running total equal at least 100 is the winner of the game.

Write a program for the game of 100.

HINTS

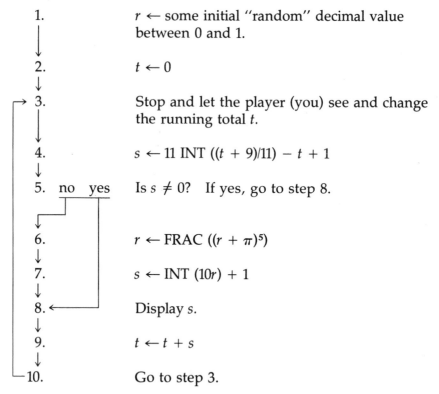

1. $r \leftarrow$ some initial "random" decimal value between 0 and 1.

2. $t \leftarrow 0$

3.   Stop and let the player (you) see and change the running total t.

4. $s \leftarrow 11$ INT $((t + 9)/11) - t + 1$

5. no yes   Is $s \neq 0$?   If yes, go to step 8.

6. $r \leftarrow$ FRAC $((r + \pi)^5)$

7. $s \leftarrow$ INT $(10r) + 1$

8.   Display s.

9. $t \leftarrow t + s$

10.   Go to step 3.

r = random real number between 0 and 1
t = game total at any time during the game
s = strategic next choice made by the machine
π = 3.141592654

COMMENTS

The loop between steps 3 to 10 creates the machine's play. When the machine has the advantage, it must play according to step 4. When the machine is not at an advantage, it makes a random play, steps 6 and 7. The test "Is $s \neq 0$?" decides whether the machine has the advantage or not.

Step 6 creates a new random decimal value between 0 and 1, and step 7 changes that value into one of the integers from 1 to 10, each occurring with equal probability.

ANSWERS AND EXTENSIONS

ANSWER: No answer required.

```
0005 REM GAME OF 100
0010 PRINT "WHAT STARTING CHOICE OF DECIMAL BETWEEN 0 AND 1";
0015 INPUT R
0020 LET I=0
0030 PRINT "RUNNING TOTAL IS ";T
0032 PRINT "WHAT DO YOU WANT TO ADD TO THE RUNNING TOTAL";
0034 INPUT S
0035 IF S<1 THEN GOTO 0037
0036 IF S<11 THEN GOTO 0039
0037 PRINT "INVALID! ADD AN INTEGER BETWEEN 1 AND 10."
0038 GOTO 0032
0039 LET I=I+S
0040 PRINT "THAT MAKES THE TOTAL ";T
0041 IF T<100 THEN GOTO 0047
0042 PRINT "YOU WIN! DO YOU WANT TO PLAY AGAIN";
0043 INPUT W$
0044 IF A$="Y" THEN GOTO 0020
0045 GOTO 0100
0047 LET S=11*INT((I+9)/11)-I+1
0050 IF S<>0 THEN GOTO 0080
0060 LET R1=(R+3.14159)^5
0065 LET R=R1-INT(R1)
0070 LET S=INT(10*R)+1
0080 PRINT "I CHOOSE TO ADD ";S
0090 LET I=I+S
0092 IF I<100 THEN GOTO 0030
0094 PRINT " I WIN WITH A TOTAL OF ";T
0095 PRINT "DO YOU WANT TO PLAY AGAIN, SAM";
0096 INPUT W$
0097 IF W$="Y" THEN GOTO 0020
0100 END
```

EXTENSIONS

A program written according to the Hints given makes your machine a formidable opponent. Unless you know the strategy (and there is one) for playing, the machine will always win. But, of course, readers will have no trouble (?) figuring out how to master their machine!

Actually, the Game of 100 can be played with any starting total (not just 0), any ending total (not just 100), and any set of consecutive integers for players' choices (not just 1 through 10). To modify the Hints to play other such games, you need to know

t = starting total
e = ending total
i = lowest play selection
and h = highest play selection for which each player can select any integer between i and h during a turn.

Next you need to calculate

a = (addition of i and h) = $i + h$
n = (number of consecutive choices for each player) = $h - i + 1$
f = (remainder of the ending total upon division by a) =
    a FRAC (e/a)
z = (strategy shift value) = $a - f - 1$

Then modify steps 2, 4, and 7 of the hints as follows:
2. $t \leftarrow$ starting total
4. $s \leftarrow a$ INT $((t+z)/a)-t+f$
5. Is ABS $(a/2 - s) < n/2$?   If yes, go to step 8.
7. $s \leftarrow$ INT$(nr) + i$

For example, to play from 1 to 70 and use the set of the players' choices between 3 and 6, use $t=1$, $e=70$, $i=3$, and $h=6$.

Next calculate

$a = 3+6=9$
$n = 6-3+1=4$
$f = 9 \cdot$ FRAC$(70/9)=7$
$z = 9-7-1=1$

Then replace steps 2, 4, and 7 of the hints with

2. $t \leftarrow 1$
4. $s \leftarrow 9$ INT $((t+1)/9)-t+7$
5. Is ABS $(4.5-s) < 2$?   If yes, go to step 8.
7. $s \leftarrow$ INT$(4r)+3$

How can you master your machine in this game?

THE POLITICANS'
BANQUET

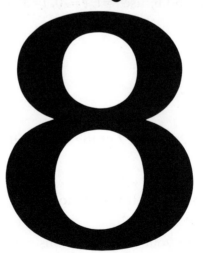

PROBLEM STATEMENT

At a fund-raising banquet, one hundred politicians and guests showed up. Each senator who attended paid $75, each congressman paid $99, and each guest paid $40. If $7,869 was collected, how many of the one hundred people were senators, congressmen, and guests, respectively?

HINTS

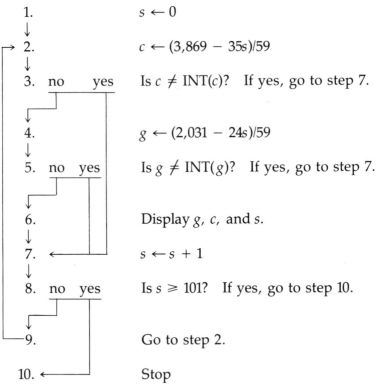

1. $s \leftarrow 0$

2. $c \leftarrow (3{,}869 - 35s)/59$

3.   no   yes   Is $c \neq \mathrm{INT}(c)$?   If yes, go to step 7.

4. $g \leftarrow (2{,}031 - 24s)/59$

5.   no   yes   Is $g \neq \mathrm{INT}(g)$?   If yes, go to step 7.

6.   Display g, c, and s.

7.   ← $s \leftarrow s + 1$

8.   no   yes   Is $s \geq 101$?   If yes, go to step 10.

9.   Go to step 2.

10. ←   Stop

s = the number of senators
c = the number of congressmen
g = the number of guests

COMMENTS

For s, c, and g representing the numbers of senators, congressmen, and guests, respectively, two equations must be satisfied:

$$75s + 99c + 40g = 7,869 \qquad \text{(dollars)}$$
$$s + c + g = 100 \qquad \text{(people)}$$

Because there cannot be any more than one hundred senators, it becomes effective to calculate, for each value of s between 0 and 100, the corresponding values of c and g so that these equations are satisfied. Therefore it makes sense to solve these equations for c and g, obtaining expressions in terms of s:

$$c = (3,869 - 35s)/59$$
$$g = (2,031 - 24s)/59$$

The loop between steps 2 and 9 starts s at 0 and increases s by 1 during each loop. As such, all values of s are produced between 0 and 100. Next, values of c and g are calculated in steps 2 and 4, respectively, according to the above equations. In the event that both c and g are integers—for example, both "Is $c \neq \text{INT}(c)$?" and "Is $g \neq \text{INT}(g)$?" have "no" for an answer—then a solution of integer values for g, c, and s has been found. This solution set is then displayed in step 6.

ANSWERS AND EXTENSIONS

ANSWERS: For values of s from 0 to 100, two sets of integers satisfy the stated conditions. They are $g = 21$, $c = 46$, $s = 33$ and $g = -3$, $c = 11$, $s = 92$. Disallowing the case where $g = -3$ (a negative number of guests in attendance is not possible), the solution is $g = 21$, $c = 46$, and $s = 33$.

```
0005 REM THE POLITICIANS BANQUET
0010 LET S=0
0020 LET C=(3869-35*S)/59
0030 IF C<>INT(C) THEN GOTO 0070
0040 LET G=(2051-24*S)/59
0050 IF G<>INT(G) THEN GOTO 0070
0060 PRINT "THERE WERE ";S;" SENATORS, ";C;" CONGRESSMEN, AND ";
0061 PRINT G;" GUESTS"
0062 PRINT "PROOF:"
0063 PRINT "  75*";S;" + 99*";C;" + 40*";G;" IS ";75*S+99*C+40*G
0064 PRINT "   AND    ";S;" + ";C;" + ";G;"  IS   ";S+C+G
0070 LET S=S+1
0080 IF S>=101 THEN GOTO 0100
0090 GOTO 0020
0100 END
```

EXTENSIONS:

i. If the amount of money collected was $9,494, how many
   of the one hundred persons were senators, congressmen, and guests? To answer this question, merely
   change steps 2 and 4 of the hints to:

   2. $c \leftarrow (5494 - 35s)/59$
   4. $g \leftarrow (406 - 24s)/59$

ii. If the amount collected was $13,180, but two hundred
   persons were present, how many were senators, congressmen, and guests? This can be answered by changing steps 2 and 4 to:

   2. $c \leftarrow (5180 - 35s)/59$
   4. $g \leftarrow (6620 - 24s)/59$

   Note that step 8 does *not* need to be changed to:

   8. Is $s \geq 201$? If yes, go to step 10.

   This is because there cannot be more than one hundred
   senators present by nature of the fact that there are only
   fifty states in the United States!

iii. If the amount collected was $6,506 and 102 persons were
   present, how many of them were senators, congressmen, and guests?

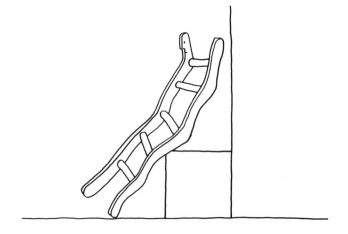

THE SUPPORTED
LADDER

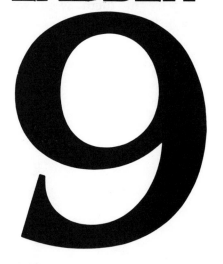

PROBLEM STATEMENT

A 5-meter ladder standing on the floor and resting against the wall is supported by a 1-meter cubical-shaped box, placed on the floor against the same wall. How high above the box does the ladder reach?

HINTS

1. $p \leftarrow$ input value, $q \leftarrow$ input value

2. $s \leftarrow p^4 + 2p^3 - 23p^2 + 2p + 1$, $t \leftarrow q^4 + 2q^3 - 23q^2 + 2q + 1$

→3. no   yes Is $\text{ABS}(p-q) < 0.000001$? If yes, go to step 9.

4. $r \leftarrow q - (p-q)(t)/(s-t)$

5. $u \leftarrow r^4 + 2r^3 - 23r^2 + 2r + 1$

6. no yes Is $\text{ABS}(s) < \text{ABS}(t)$? If yes, go to step 8.

7. $p \leftarrow r$, $s \leftarrow u$. Go to step 3.

8. $q \leftarrow r$, $t \leftarrow u$. Go to step 3.

9. Display q. Stop.

p and q = distinct initial guesses of the desired root of the equation that will solve the supported ladder problem. Note: p and q must not be equal to each other.

r = improved approximation to the root

$s, t,$ and u = the polynominal values corresponding to p, q, and r, respectively

COMMENTS

Relevant distances can be labeled as in the diagram:

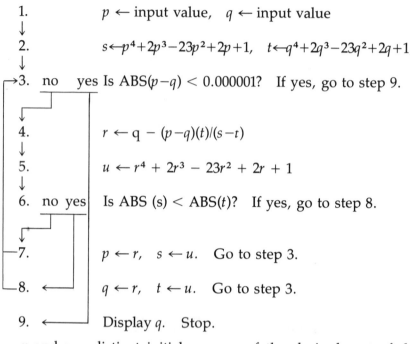

Similar triangles establish

$$\frac{y}{1} = \frac{1}{x}$$

and the Pythagorean theorem requires

$$(x + 1)^2 + (y + 1)^2 = 5^2$$

Therefore

$$(x + 1)^2 + (\frac{1}{x} + 1)^2 = 25$$

which can be written as:

$$x^4 + 2x^3 - 23x^2 + 2x + 1 = 0$$

The hints are designed to find real roots to this last equation using a method known as the "variable secant" or "reguli falsi" iteration technique.

Step 1 of the Hints uses two different initial guesses, p and q, for the required distance. From those values it calculates the corresponding values, s and t, for the polynomial, $x^4+2x^3-23x^2+2x+1$, which occurs as the left-hand side of the last equation. The loop between steps 3 and 8 forms an improved approximation, r, to a root of that polynomial (according to the variable secant method). It then calculates the corresponding polynomial value, u.

During each loop, a new value of r is calculated by adjusting q using information from both p and q (step 4). As the looping proceeds, p and q become closer and closer together. When they are essentially equal—when "Is ABS(p-q) <0.000001?" has a "yes" answer—q no longer needs to be adjusted, and the looping can be stopped (step 3). You may try the alternate questions: "Is ABS(p-q) < 0.00000001?" or "Is $p = q$?" These give more accuracy on some machines and an infinite looping process on others.

ANSWERS AND EXTENSIONS

ANSWERS: All the roots to the supported ladder equation

$$x^4 + 2x^3 - 23x^2 + 2x + 1 = 0$$

are 3.8385012, 0.26051835, −0.16862278, and −5.9303967 approximately. With initial guesses of $p=3$ and $q=4$, the larger positive root is found. The other positive root can be found by starting with $p=1$ and $q=2$.

So the ladder is resting in either of two positions so that the top of the ladder is either 3.84 meters or 0.26 meters above the top of the box.

```
0005 REM THE SUPPORTED LADDER
0010 PRINT "WHAT IS ONE GUESS";
0011 INPUT P
0015 PRINT "WHAT IS A SECOND GUESS";
0016 INPUT Q
0020 DEF FNA(X)=(((X+2)*X-23)*X+2)*X+1
0025 LET S=FNA(P)
0027 LET T=FNA(Q)
0030 IF ABS(P-Q)<.000001 THEN GOTO 0090
0040 LET R=Q-T*(P-Q)/(S-T)
0050 LET U=FNA(R)
0060 IF ABS(S)<ABS(T) THEN GOTO 0080
0070 LET P=R
0072 LET S=U
0074 GOTO 0030
0080 LET Q=R
0082 LET T=U
0084 GOTO 0030
0090 PRINT Q
0100 END
```

EXTENSIONS:

The hint in this problem gives a general technique for finding the real roots of most equations of the form $f(x) = 0$. By merely changing steps 2 and 5 to:

2. $s \leftarrow f(p), \quad t \leftarrow f(q)$
5. $u \leftarrow f(r)$.

For example, to find the three real roots of $x^3 - 2.1x^2 - 7.42 + 10.2$, change steps 2 and 5 to:

2. $s \leftarrow p^3 - 2.1p^2 - 7.42p + 10.2,$
   $t \leftarrow q^3 - 2.1q^2 - 7.42q - 10.2$
5. $u \leftarrow r^3 - 2.1r^2 - 7.42r + 10.2$

What are the roots?

THE POSTAGE STAMP PROBLEM

PROBLEM

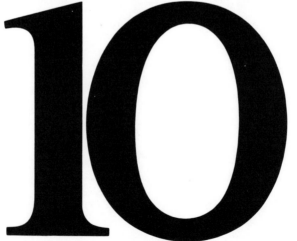

PROBLEM STATEMENT

Cost-conscious Claire never likes to send letters when the cost of the stamps is more than it needs to be. She has lots of 15¢ and 13¢ stamps because sending any first-class letter requires 15¢ for the first ounce and 13¢ for every other ounce. Today Claire just wrote a one-ounce letter to her grandmother in France. She called the post office and learned that it costs 31¢ per half-ounce to send a letter first class air mail to Europe. Thus, her one-ounce letter requires 62¢ to mail. Unfortunately, Claire cannot make the 62¢ cost using just her 15¢ and 13¢ stamps. So she walked to the post office to purchase the correct amount.

On the way, Claire wondered what would be the largest dollar and cents value that would cause her to have to go to the post office to purchase other stamps. What is that value?

HINTS

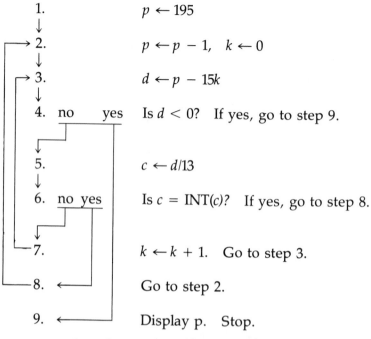

1. $p \leftarrow 195$

2. $p \leftarrow p - 1$, $k \leftarrow 0$

3. $d \leftarrow p - 15k$

4. no   yes   Is $d < 0$?   If yes, go to step 9.

5. $c \leftarrow d/13$

6. no yes   Is $c = \text{INT}(c)$?   If yes, go to step 8.

7. $k \leftarrow k + 1$.   Go to step 3.

8. $\leftarrow$ Go to step 2.

9. $\leftarrow$ Display p.   Stop.

p = current postage amount being tested
k = current multiple of 15 for test purposes
c = current multiple of 13 for test purposes
d = current value of 13c

COMMENTS

The loop between steps 3 and 7 decides whether the current p value can be formed as non-negative combinations of 15 and 13. Such a combination is found when the test "Is $c = $ INT(c)?" has a "yes" answer. All combinations have been exhausted, and no combination is possible when the other test "Is $d < 0$?" obtains a "yes" answer.

The loop between steps 2 and 8 repeats the inner loop for decreasing values of p starting at one less than the product $(15)(13) = 195$.

Actually the Hints locate the largest value of p less than the product of 15 and 13 for which no non-negative combination is possible. Since 15 and 13 have no common factor, it can be shown mathematically that every number bigger than the product can be formed as a non-negative combination of 15 and 13. Therefore, the answer provided by the hints is truely the largest possible value of p and hence provides a solution to the problem.

ANSWERS AND EXTENSIONS

ANSWERS: The largest dollars and cents value that would force Claire to go to the post office to purchase other stamps is $1.67.

```
0005 REM THE POSTAGE STAMP PROBLEM
0010 LET P=195
0020 LET P=P-1
0025 LET K=0
0030 LET D=P-15*K
0040 IF D<0 THEN GOTO 0090
0050 LET C=D/13
0060 IF C=INT(C) THEN GOTO 0080
0070 LET K=K+1
0075 GOTO 0030
0080 GOTO 0020
0090 PRINT P
0100 END
```

EXTENSIONS:

  i. By changing steps 1, 3, and 5 in the Hints, you can find the largest number that cannot be formed with non-negative combinations of any two whole numbers, as long as they have no common factor. Specifically, with numbers *a* and *b*, where *a* is the bigger number, change the steps to:

      1. $p \leftarrow ab$
      3. $d \leftarrow p\text{-}ak$
      5. $c \leftarrow d/b$

    For example, to find the largest number that cannot be formed with (non-negative) combinations of 18 and 25, use $a=25$ and $b=18$. What is this largest number?

  ii. What is the largest postage amount that cannot be formed with non-negative combinations of 11¢ and 4¢ stamps?

 iii. By running the program for various choices of *a* and *b*, collect data and guess a formula, in terms of *a* and *b*, for the smallest number not attainable from (non-negative) combinations of *a* and *b*.

PERSISTENCE NUMBERS

11

PROBLEM STATEMENT

Multiplying the digits of an integer and continuing the process gives the surprising result that the sequence of products always arrives at a single-digit number. For example,

715 ➤ 35 ➤ 15 ➤ 5
88 ➤ 64 ➤ 24 ➤ 8
27 ➤ 14 ➤ 4

The number of products necessary to reach the single-digit is called the persistence number of that integer. Thus, 715 and 88 have persistence 3, while 27 has persistence 2.

What is the only two-digit integer with persistence greater than 3?

HINTS

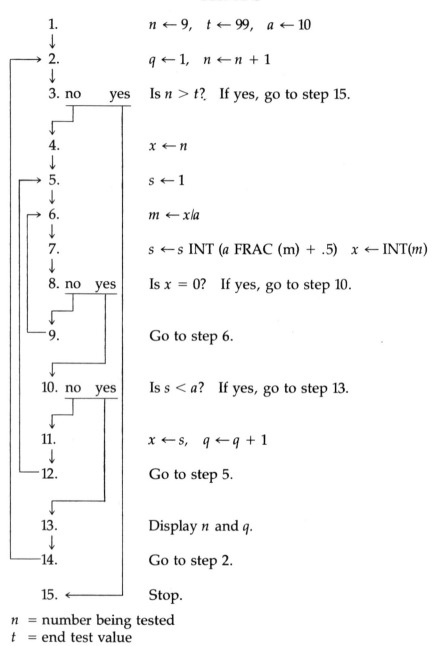

1.
   $n \leftarrow 9, \quad t \leftarrow 99, \quad a \leftarrow 10$

2.
   $q \leftarrow 1, \quad n \leftarrow n + 1$

3. no   yes   Is $n > t$? If yes, go to step 15.

4.
   $x \leftarrow n$

5.
   $s \leftarrow 1$

6.
   $m \leftarrow x/a$

7.
   $s \leftarrow s$ INT $(a$ FRAC $(m) + .5)$ $x \leftarrow$ INT(m)

8. no   yes   Is $x = 0$? If yes, go to step 10.

9.
   Go to step 6.

10. no   yes   Is $s < a$? If yes, go to step 13.

11.
   $x \leftarrow s, \quad q \leftarrow q + 1$

12.
   Go to step 5.

13.
   Display n and q.

14.
   Go to step 2.

15. ←
   Stop.

n = number being tested
t = end test value
a = 10

q = persistence number for n
x = current remaining part of n or of previous product of digits of n
s = current product of digits of n
m = temporary value of x shifted one decimal place.

COMMENTS

The loop between steps 6 and 9 picks off all the digits from x one by one and creates their product, s. The test "Is $x = 0$?" decides whether more digits need to be picked off or not.

The loop between steps 5 and 12 produces the persistence number, q, for any specific number n. It does this by counting the number of times it needs to repeat the previous loop in order to produce a single digit product, s. The test "Is $s < a$?" decides whether s is a single digit or not.

The loop between steps 2 and 14 finds the persistence number for each number between 10 and 99.

ANSWERS AND EXTENSIONS

ANSWER: The integer 77 has persistence number 4 and is the only two-digit number with a persistence number greater than 3.

```
0005 REM PERSISTENCE NUMBERS
0010 LET N=9
0013 LET T=99
0017 LET A=10
0020 LET Q=1
0025 LET N=N+1
0030 IF N>T THEN GOTO 0150
0040 LET X=N
0050 LET S=1
0060 LET M=X/A
0070 LET S=INT(S*A*(M-INT(M))+.5)
0075 LET X=INT(M)
0080 IF X=0 THEN GOTO 0100
0090 GOTO 0060
0100 IF S<A THEN GOTO 0130
0110 LET X=S
0115 LET Q=Q+1
0120 GOTO 0050
0130 PRINT N;" HAS PERSISTENCE NUMBER ";Q
0140 GOTO 0020
0150 END
```

EXTENSIONS:

i. The Hints produce the persistence number for integers between 10 and 99. By changing the input data in step 1, you can find the persistence number of other integers. For instance, to examine all three-digit numbers, change step 1 to:

$$1. \; n \leftarrow 99, \quad t \leftarrow 999, \quad a \leftarrow 0$$

ii. What are the smallest numbers with persistence numbers 2, 3, 4, and 5, respectively? To answer this, run the program you designed from the Hints.

iii. Persistence numbers as defined in the problem come from a multiplicative property. The digits of n are multiplied together. You may explore additive persistence, that is, the case where the digits of n, are added together at each stage (rather than multiplied). You will need to modify steps 5 and 7 of the Hints as follows:

$$5. \; s \leftarrow 0$$
$$7. \; s \leftarrow s + \text{INT} \, (a\text{FRAC}(m) + .5), \quad x \leftarrow \text{INT}(m)$$

THE HIGH–LOW
GAME

12

PROBLEM STATEMENT

Here is a popular two-person game that could be played on a simple calculator with a constant feature for division. Program your machine to be the first player. Play the game, and see if you can develop a strategy for always identifying the number in the minimum number of guesses.

1. The first player enters a positive two-digit integer in the calculator display, then presses ÷, =, and 0 in that order.
2. The second player enters a guess in the calculator display and presses the = key. If the result in the display is greater than 1, the guess is too high. If the result in the display is less than 1, the guess is too low. In either case, this player continues entering guesses and pressing the = key.
3. When the second player's guess is correct, 1 appears in the display.

HINTS

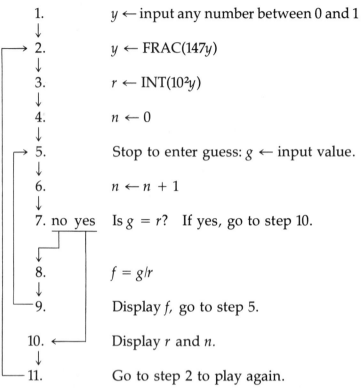

1. $y \leftarrow$ input any number between 0 and 1

2. $y \leftarrow$ FRAC(147y)

3. $r \leftarrow$ INT($10^2 y$)

4. $n \leftarrow 0$

5.   Stop to enter guess: $g \leftarrow$ input value.

6. $n \leftarrow n + 1$

7. no yes   Is $g = r$? If yes, go to step 10.

8. $f = g/r$

9.   Display f, go to step 5.

10.   Display r and n.

11.   Go to step 2 to play again.

y = any decimal number between 0 and 1 to be used as a "seed" for the random number generator
n = the total number of guesses
g = the current guess
f = the output ratio
r = a random two-digit number

COMMENTS

Steps 2 and 3 create a random two-digit number from a "seed" number with the first "seed" provided in step 1. Then a new "seed" is created in step 2, from which the two-digit random number is produced in step 3.

The loop between steps 5 and 9 allows each new guess to be inputed, tallied, and compared to the random two-digit number. If unequal—that is, if "'Is g = r?" has a "no" answer—the ratio of *g* to *r* is displayed, and the steps loop to allow a new guess to be made.

If a guess equals the random number, both the random number *r* and the tally of guesses *n* are displayed (step 10). Then the steps loop to obtain a new random two-digit number in order for the game to continue.

ANSWERS AND EXTENSIONS

ANSWERS: You can always identify the number after the first guess by merely taking the result shown and dividing it into your guess. But, of course, the game then becomes less fun to play.

```
0005 REM HIGH-LOW GAME
0010 PRINT "WHAT'S A RANDOM DECIMAL BETWEEN 0 AND 1";
0015 INPUT Y
0020 LET Y=147*Y-INT(147*Y)
0030 LET R=INT(100*Y)
0040 LET N=0
0050 PRINT "WHAT'S YOUR GUESS";
0055 INPUT G
0060 LET N=N+1
0070 IF G=R THEN GOTO 0100
0080 LET F=G/R
0090 PRINT F
0095 GOTO 0050
0100 PRINT "YOU GUESSED ";R;" IN ";N;" GUESSES!"
0110 GOTO 0020
0120 END
```

EXTENSIONS:

i. You can have the program generate random numbers with however many digits you like, within the limits of your machine, by merely varying the power of ten in the appropriate expression in step 2 of the Hints. Thus, step 2 becomes

$$2.\ y \leftarrow \text{FRAC}(147y), \quad r = \text{INT}(10^a y)$$

where a is the desired number of digits.

ii. As noted above, the fun of playing this game disappears if you know the strategy for guessing given in the answer. In order to disguise the message that your machine gives, change the Hints as follows:

$$8.\ f \leftarrow (g/r)^{1,000}$$

or

$$8.\ f \leftarrow (g/r)^{10,000}$$

The effect of this change is to display a huge number if your guess is too high or to display 0 or a very small number if your guess is too low.

Now, what strategy would you use to identify the number in the fewest number of guesses?

THE FOOTBALL JERSEYS

13

PROBLEM STATEMENT

Two friends play on the same football team. Each has his own team number that he wears on his jersey. One day their coach notices the surprising fact that the square of the sum of their respective numbers is, in fact, the four-digit number that he sees when they stand along side of one another. Thus, the numbers are not, for instance, 17 and 23, since $17 + 23 = 40$ and $40^2 \neq 1{,}723$.

What can their numbers be?

HINTS

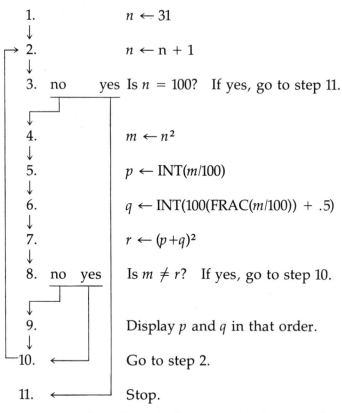

1. $n \leftarrow 31$

2. $n \leftarrow n + 1$

3.   no   yes   Is $n = 100$?   If yes, go to step 11.

4. $m \leftarrow n^2$

5. $p \leftarrow \text{INT}(m/100)$

6. $q \leftarrow \text{INT}(100(\text{FRAC}(m/100)) + .5)$

7. $r \leftarrow (p+q)^2$

8.   no   yes   Is $m \neq r$?   If yes, go to step 10.

9.   Display p and q in that order.

10.   ←   Go to step 2.

11.   ←   Stop.

m = current four-digit perfect square being tested
n = $\sqrt{m}$
p = the number formed from the two left-most digits of m
q = the number formed from the two right-most digits of m
r = $(p+q)^2$

COMMENTS

The loop between steps 2 and 10 looks at each four-digit square number m and decides whether it equals the square of the sum of its two-digit left and right halves. Specifically, steps 5 and 6 pick off the left and right pairs of digits of n, and step 7 recomposes those numbers to form r. The test "Is $m \neq r$?" decides whether the original four-digit square does or does not have the property that surprised the coach.

Since the four-digit number m is necessarily a square, that number can be called n^2. Furthermore, because n^2 has four digits,

$$1{,}000 \leqslant n^2 < 10{,}000$$

and

$$31.6 \leqslant n < 100.$$

Thus n starts at 32 and increases by 1 each time through the loop until it becomes 100. In that way, all four-digit perfect squares $m = n^2$ are efficiently formed and checked.

ANSWERS AND EXTENSIONS

ANSWER: Mathematically there are three solutions:

$$(20 + 25)^2 = 2,025$$
$$(30 + 25)^2 = 3,025$$
$$\text{and } (98 + 01)^2 = 9,801$$

However, the number 01 is not used on a football practice shirt; the digit 1 is used instead. So it is necessary that the friend standing on the right had number 25 while the other friend had number 20 or 30.

```
0005 REM THE FOOTBALL JERSEYS
0010 LET N=31
0020 LET N=N+1
0030 IF N=100 THEN GOTO 0110
0040 LET M=N*N
0050 LET P=INT(M/100)
0060 LET Q=INT(100*(M/100-INT(M/100))+.5)
0070 LET R=(P+Q)*(P+Q)
0080 IF M<>R THEN GOTO 0100
0090 PRINT P;Q
0100 GOTO 0020
0110 END
```

EXTENSIONS

i. By changing step 7 in the Hints to

$$7. \ r \leftarrow (p - q)^2$$

you can see if there are any four-digit numbers $abcd$, such that $(ab - cd)^2 = abcd$.

Are there any four-digit numbers with this property?

ii. By changing step 7 of the Hints to

$$7. \ r \leftarrow (4(p-q))^2$$

you can see if there are any four-digit integers $abcd$, such that $(4(ab - cd))^2 = abcd$.

Which four-digit numbers have this property?

iii. Do any pairs of three-digit numbers have the football jersey property? That is, do any two three-digit numbers, p and q, have the property that $(p + q)^2 =$ "p written next to q"? Change steps 1, 3, 5, and 6 of the Hints to the following in order to answer this question.

1. $n \leftarrow 316$
3. Is $n = 1000$? If yes, go to step 11.
5. $p \leftarrow$ INT $(m/1000)$
6. $q \leftarrow$ INT $(1,000 \text{FRAC}(m/1000) + .5)$

INTRIGUING INTEGERS

PROBLEM STATEMENT

a. Which three consecutive integers have a product that is 800 times their sum?
b. Which three consecutive even integers have a sum that is equal to 1/132 of their product?
c. Which three consecutive odd integers give a perfect square when their product is added to their sum plus 9?

HINTS

1. $a \leftarrow 0$

2. $a \leftarrow a + 1$

3. $b \leftarrow a + 1, \quad c \leftarrow a + 2$

4. $m \leftarrow abc, \quad n \leftarrow 800\,(a + b + c)$

5.   no   yes   Is $n = m$?   If yes, go to step 7.

6.   Go to step 2.

7.   Display the integers. Stop.

a = first integer
b = second integer
c = third integer
m = abc
n = $800\,(a + b + c)$

COMMENTS

The loop in steps 2 through 6, starts a counting number a at 1 and increases it by 1 each time through the loop. It then loops indefinitely until finding the first solution of the form

$$a\,(a+1)\,(a+2) = 800\,((a) + (a+1) + (a+2))$$

To solve problem b, change steps 2, 3 and 4 in the Hints to
  2. $a \leftarrow a+2$
  3. $b \leftarrow a+2, \quad c \leftarrow a+4$
  4. $m \leftarrow a+b+c, \quad n \leftarrow (1/132)\,(abc)$
To solve problem c, change steps 1 to 5 and add 5.5 in the hints to
  1. $a \leftarrow -1$
  2. $a \leftarrow a+2$
  3. $b \leftarrow a+2, \quad c \leftarrow a+4$
  4. $m \leftarrow abc + (a+b+c)+9$
  5. $r \leftarrow \mathrm{INT}\,(\sqrt{m} + .5)$
  5.5 Is $(r)(r) = m$? If yes, go to step 7.

ANSWERS AND EXTENSIONS

ANSWERS:

a. The consecutive integers are 48, 49 and 50.

b. The consecutive even integers are 18, 20 and 22.

c. The solution is not unique. Some of the consecutive odd integers are 7, 9, 11; 33, 35, 37; 35, 37, 39; and 315, 317, 319.

a.
```
0005 REM INTRIGUING INTEGERS
0010 LET A=0
0020 LET A=A+1
0030 LET B=A+1
0035 LET C=A+2
0040 LET M=A*B*C
0045 LET N=800*(A+B+C)
0050 IF N=M THEN GOTO 0070
0060 GOTO 0020
0070 PRINT A,B,C
0080 END
```

b.
```
0005 REM INTRIGUING INTEGERS
0010 LET A=0
0020 LET A=A+2
0030 LET B=A+2
0035 LET C=A+4
0040 LET M=A+B+C
0045 LET N=(1/132)*A*B*C
0050 IF N=M THEN GOTO 0070
0060 GOTO 0020
0070 PRINT A,B,C
0080 END
```

c.
```
0005 REM INTRIGUING INTEGERS
0010 LET A=-1
0020 LET A=A+2
0030 LET B=A+2
0035 LET C=A+4
0040 LET M=A*B*C+(A+B+C)+9
0050 IF SQR(M)=INT(SQR(M)) THEN GOTO 0070
0060 GOTO 0020
0070 PRINT A,B,C
0080 END
```

EXTENSIONS

i. For which set of 3 consecutive integers n, $n+1$, and $n+2$ is $n(n+1)(n+2) = 10n(n + (n+1) + (n+2))$? To explore this problem, change step 4 in the Hint to

4. $m \leftarrow abc$, $\quad n \leftarrow 10a(a+b+c)$

ii. For which set of 4 consecutive integers n, $n+1$, $n+2$, and $n+3$ is the product plus 8 a perfect cube? To explore this problem, change steps 3, 4, and 5 to

3. $b \leftarrow a+1$, $\quad c \leftarrow a+2$, $\quad d \leftarrow a+3$
4. $m \leftarrow abcd + 8$, $n \leftarrow$ INT $(m^{1/3} + .5)$
5. Is $m = (n)(n)(n)$? If yes, go to step 7.

FINDING
UNIT FRACTIONS
15

PROBLEM STATEMENT

Certain fractions can be written as the sum of two fractions each with numerator one. For example,

$$9/20 = (1/5) + (1/4)$$
$$1/2 = (1/3) + (1/6)$$
$$10/21 = (1/3) + (1/7)$$

Some of the following fractions cannot be written in this way. Which are they?

  a. 5/36
  b. 5/37
  c. 5/38
  d. 20/91
  e. 13/63

HINTS

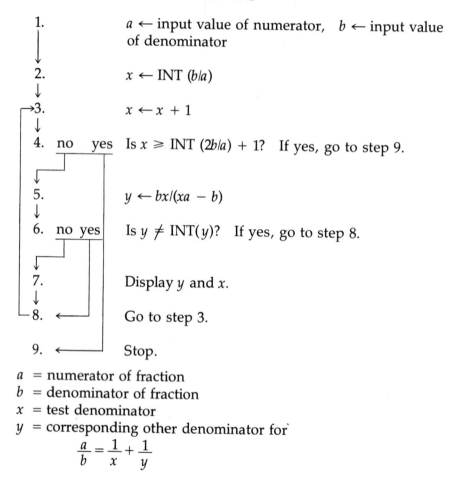

1. $a \leftarrow$ input value of numerator, $b \leftarrow$ input value of denominator

2. $x \leftarrow$ INT (b/a)

3. $x \leftarrow x + 1$

4.   no   yes Is $x \geqslant$ INT $(2b/a) + 1$?   If yes, go to step 9.

5. $y \leftarrow bx/(xa - b)$

6.   no yes   Is $y \neq$ INT(y)?   If yes, go to step 8.

7.   Display y and x.

8. $\leftarrow$ Go to step 3.

9. $\leftarrow$ Stop.

a = numerator of fraction
b = denominator of fraction
x = test denominator
y = corresponding other denominator for
$$\frac{a}{b} = \frac{1}{x} + \frac{1}{y}$$

COMMENTS

The loop between steps 3 and 8 creates various integers x and calculates the corresponding y value according to

$$y = bx/(xa-b)$$

which is another version of the desired equation:

$$\frac{a}{b} = \frac{1}{x} + \frac{1}{y}$$

In order to start and end the loop appropriately, two inequalities help. First, the obvious inequality

$$\frac{a}{b} = \frac{1}{x} + \frac{1}{y} > \frac{1}{x}$$

leads to $x>b/a$ and $x>\text{INT}(b/a)$. Second, with x always being the smaller of the two denominators, $1/x$ is the larger of the unit fractions $1/x$ and $1/y$ so that

$$\frac{a}{b} = \frac{1}{x} + \frac{1}{y} \leqslant \frac{1}{x} + \frac{1}{x} = \frac{2}{x}$$

This leads to $x \leqslant 2b/a$ and $x \leqslant \text{INT}(2b/a)$. Therefore the loop starts x at $\text{INT}(b/a)+1$, increases x by one each time and ends when x exceeds $\text{INT}(2b/a)$.

ANSWERS AND EXTENSIONS

ANSWER: The fractions 5/37 and 13/63 cannot be written as the sum of two unit fractions. The fraction 5/36 can be done in three ways as (1/72) + (1/8); (1/36)+(1/9); and (1/18)+(1/12). The fractions 5/38 and 20/91 can each be done in one way as (1/8)+(1/152) and (1/7)+(1/13), respectively.

```
0005 REM FINDING UNIT FRACTIONS
0010 PRINT "WHAT NUMERATOR";
0012 INPUT A
0015 PRINT "WHAT DENOMINATOR";
0017 INPUT B
0020 LET X=INT(B/A)
0030 LET X=X+1
0040 IF X>=INT(2*B/A)+1 THEN GOTO 0090
0050 LET Y=B*X/(X*A-B)
0060 IF Y<>INT(Y) THEN GOTO 0080
0070 PRINT A;"/";B;" EQUALS  1/";X;" +   1/";Y
0080 GOTO 0030
0090 END
```

EXTENSIONS:

With the Hint given for this problem, you can explore many interesting questions about unit fractions. Here are some:

    i. Consider the fractions 1/2, 1/3, 1/4, 1/5, ... What is the smallest denominator for which the fraction can be expressed as the sum of two unit fractions in at least four ways?

    ii. If you order the fractions as 1/2, 2/4, 3/8, 4/16, . . . $n/2^2$ what is the first such fraction that can be represented as two unit fractions in more than three ways?

    iii. Consider the fraction 5/360, which can be expressed as the sum of two unit fractions in many ways. Which of these ways gives the smallest product of denominators?

$$8833 = 88^2 + 33^2$$

THE TIME OF DAY
16

PROBLEM STATEMENT

In her mathematics class, Professor Harrison was talking about interesting properties of integers. She showed the class the number 8,833 which equals $88^2 + 33^2$ and proceeded with her lecture.

As students are likely to do, clever Cleveland paid less than full attention to Professor Harrison's lecture and was, instead, watching the digital wall clock. He noticed that when Professor Harrison finished talking about 8,833, the time on the clock (viewed as a number without the colon) had the same property. That is, the square of the hours' digit(s) plus the square of the minutes' digit(s) equaled the number he saw.

What was the time of day?

HINTS

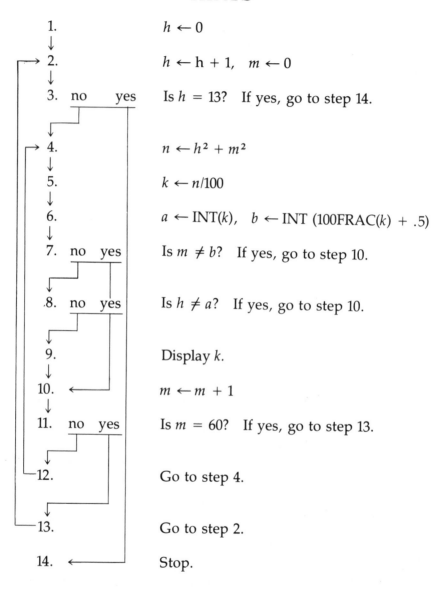

1. $h \leftarrow 0$

2. $h \leftarrow h + 1, \quad m \leftarrow 0$

3.   no   yes   Is $h = 13$?   If yes, go to step 14.

4. $n \leftarrow h^2 + m^2$

5. $k \leftarrow n/100$

6. $a \leftarrow \text{INT}(k), \quad b \leftarrow \text{INT}(100\text{FRAC}(k) + .5)$

7.   no   yes   Is $m \neq b$?   If yes, go to step 10.

8.   no   yes   Is $h \neq a$?   If yes, go to step 10.

9.   Display k.

10. $m \leftarrow m + 1$

11.   no   yes   Is $m = 60$?   If yes, go to step 13.

12.   Go to step 4.

13.   Go to step 2.

14.   Stop.

h = the number of hours	k = n shifted two decimal places
m = the number of minutes	a = the one or two left-most digits
n = sum of squares of h and m	b = the one or two right-most digits

COMMENTS

The loop between steps 2 and 13 starts the number of hours h at 1, increases h by 1 during each loop, and ends when $h > 12$. Similarly the loop between steps 4 and 12 starts the number of minutes m at 0, increases m by one during each loop, and ends when $m \geqslant 60$.

For each created set of values of h and m, the number n is formed according to

$$n = h^2 + m^2$$

Then steps 5 and 6 separate as in step 4 off the right-most two digits of n so that the various parts a and b can be compared to h and m, respectively. When both $m=b$ and $h=a$, the special time of day is found.

ANSWERS AND EXTENSIONS

ANSWER: Since $1,233^2 = 12^2 + 33^2$ is the only other number that appears on a digital clock with this property, the time of day was 12:33 PM. It is unlikely that Professor Harrison's class would meet after midnight!

```
0005 REM THE TIME OF DAY
0010 LET H=0
0020 LET H=H+1
0025 LET M=0
0030 IF H=13 THEN GOTO 0140
0040 LET N=H*H+M*M
0050 LET K=N/100
0060 LET A=INT(K)
0065 LET B=INT(100*(K-INT(K))+.5)
0070 IF M<>B THEN GOTO 0100
0080 IF H<>A THEN GOTO 0100
0090 PRINT " THE TIME OF DAY WAS ";K
0100 LET M=M+1
0110 IF M=60 THEN GOTO 0130
0120 GOTO 0040
0130 GOTO 0020
0140 END
```

EXTENSION:

To check all four-digit numbers to see whether there are any others like 1,233 and 8,833, make the following changes in steps 1, 9, and 13 in the Hints:

  1. $h \leftarrow 0$
  3. Is $h = 100$? If yes, go to step 14.
11. Is $m = 100$? If yes, go to step 13.
Are there any other four-digit numbers of this type?

HOW BIG IS
THE FLEET?
17

PROBLEM STATEMENT

The owner of Turtle Trucking Company is an amateur mathematician. After buying a new fleet of trucks, he decides to identify each vehicle by painting some number less than 500 on each cab. Just to be different, he chooses all the numbers whose square ends in the number. Thus, one of the trucks was numbered 25 since $25^2 = 625$.

How many trucks were in the Turtle Trucking Company's fleet? And what were their numbers?

HINTS

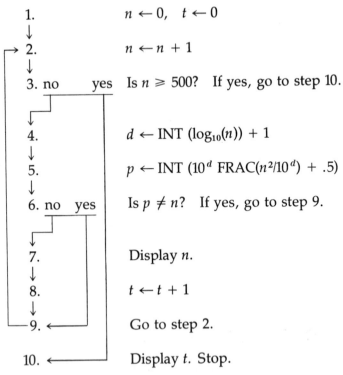

1.	$n \leftarrow 0, \quad t \leftarrow 0$
2.	$n \leftarrow n + 1$
3. no yes	Is $n \geqslant 500$? If yes, go to step 10.
4.	$d \leftarrow \text{INT} (\log_{10}(n)) + 1$
5.	$p \leftarrow \text{INT} (10^d \, \text{FRAC}(n^2/10^d) + .5)$
6. no yes	Is $p \neq n$? If yes, go to step 9.
7.	Display n.
8.	$t \leftarrow t + 1$
9.	Go to step 2.
10.	Display t. Stop.

n = current integer being tested
d = number of digits in n
p = 10^d
t = total number of digits with the desired property

COMMENTS

The loop between steps 2 and 9 starts n at 1, increases n by 1 each time through, and ends when n has more than three digits. During each loop, the number of digits of n is computed in step 4. Next the right-most half of the digits of n^2 are created in step 5. The test "is $p \neq n$?" then decides whether those right-most half of the digits of n^2 are different from n. Whenever those digits are the same as n, a counter is increased by one to tally that occurrence.

Note the log function in step 4 refers to the base 10 logarithm. If instead of such a logarithm function, a natural logarithm (called "ALOG" in FORTRAN and "LOG" in BASIC) is available, compute $\log_{10}(n)$ using the formula:

$$\log_{10}(n) = \frac{\text{natural log } (n)}{\text{natural log } (10)}$$

ANSWERS AND EXTENSIONS

ANSWER: The fleet, admittedly not large, has six trucks numbered: 1, 5, 6, 25, 76, and 376.

```
0005 REM HOW BIG IS THE FLEET
0010 LET N=0
0015 LET T=0
0020 LET N=N+1
0030 IF N>=500 THEN GOTO 0100
0040 LET D=INT(LOG(N)/LOG(10))+1
0050 LET P=INT(10^D*(N*N/10^D-INT(N*N/10^D))+.5)
0060 IF P<>N THEN GOTO 0090
0070 PRINT "TRUCK NUMBER";N
0080 LET T=T+1
0090 GOTO 0020
0100 PRINT "TOTAL NUMBER OF TRUCKS IN THE FLEET IS ";T
0110 END
```

EXTENSIONS:

i. If the owner of Turtle Trucking allowed any number up to 1,000 to identify vehicles, how many additional trucks could he add to the fleet? To answer this question, change steps 1 and 3 in the Hints to

    1. $n \leftarrow 499$, $t \leftarrow 0$
    3. Is $n \geqslant 1000$?   If yes, go to step 10.

ii. Are there any numbers whose cubes end in the number? To explore this problem for, say, integers less than 500, merely change step 5 in the hints to

    5. $p \leftarrow$ INT $(10^{d}\text{FRAC}(n^3/10^{d}) + .5)$

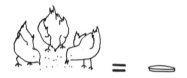

THE FOWL PROBLEM

18

PROBLEM STATEMENT

An old Chinese problem about 100 fowl goes like this. If a rooster is worth 5 coins, if a hen is worth 3 coins, and if three chicks are worth 1 coin, how many roosters, hens, chicks (100 in all and at least some of each kind) will be worth 100 coins?

HINTS

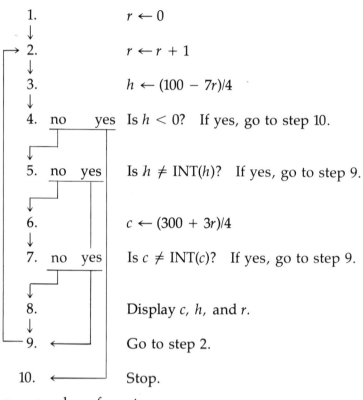

1. $r \leftarrow 0$

2. $r \leftarrow r + 1$

3. $h \leftarrow (100 - 7r)/4$

4. no yes Is $h < 0$? If yes, go to step 10.

5. no yes Is $h \neq \text{INT}(h)$? If yes, go to step 9.

6. $c \leftarrow (300 + 3r)/4$

7. no yes Is $c \neq \text{INT}(c)$? If yes, go to step 9.

8. Display c, h, and r.

9. Go to step 2.

10. Stop.

r = number of roosters
h = number of hens
c = number of chicks

COMMENTS

The Hints are based on the concept of finding positive integer values r, h, and c that satisfy:

$$5r + 3h + \frac{1}{3}c = 100$$
$$r + h + c = 100$$

or when solved for h and c:

$$h = (100-7r)/4$$
$$c = (300+3r)/4$$

The loop between steps 2 and 9 checks increasing values of r starting at 1, calculates values of h and c according to the equations above and decides whether both of those values are whole numbers. Since h decreases as r increases, the test "Is $h < 0$?" decides whether it is necessary to check any more values.

ANSWERS AND EXTENSIONS

ANSWERS: There are three solution sets to this problem. There are either

1. 4 roosters, 18 hens, and 78 chicks; or
2. 8 roosters, 11 hens, and 81 chickens; or
3. 12 roosters, 4 hens, and 84 chicks.

```
0005 REM THE FOWL PROBLEM
0010 LET R=0
0020 LET R=R+1
0030 LET H=(100-7*R)/4
0040 IF H<0 THEN GOTO 0100
0050 IF H<>INT(H) THEN GOTO 0090
0060 LET C=(300+3*R)/4
0070 IF C<>INT(C) THEN GOTO 0090
0080 PRINT " THERE WERE ";R;" ROOSTERS, ";H;" HENS, AND ";
0085 PRINT C;" CHICKS"
0090 GOTO 0020
0100 END
```

EXTENSION:

If the total number of roosters, hens, and chicks is changed from 100 to 200, the problem has two solutions. They may be found by changing steps 3 and 6 of the Hints to:

  3. $h \leftarrow (50 - 7r)/4$
  6. $c \leftarrow (750 + 3r)/4$

Can you find these solutions?

+

= $1.75

HAMBURGERS, FRENCH FRIES, AND A COKE

19

PROBLEM STATEMENT

The local hamburger stand sponsored a little competition to stimulate business. They offered a free dinner to the first five persons who could solve the following problem. Can you?

1. A hamburger costs more than two orders of french fries.
2. Three orders of french fries cost more than a hamburger and a coke.
3. Three cokes cost more than a hamburger.
4. A hamburger, one order of french fries, and a coke cost $1.75.

If the price of each item is a multiple of 5 cents, how much does each cost?

HINTS

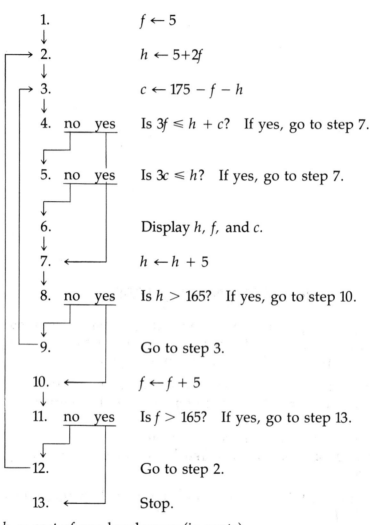

1. $f \leftarrow 5$

2. $h \leftarrow 5+2f$

3. $c \leftarrow 175 - f - h$

4. no yes   Is $3f \leq h + c$?   If yes, go to step 7.

5. no yes   Is $3c \leq h$?   If yes, go to step 7.

6.   Display h, f, and c.

7. ← $h \leftarrow h + 5$

8. no yes   Is $h > 165$?   If yes, go to step 10.

9.   Go to step 3.

10. ← $f \leftarrow f + 5$

11. no yes   Is $f > 165$?   If yes, go to step 13.

12.   Go to step 2.

13. ←   Stop.

h = cost of one hamburger (in cents)
f = cost of one order of french fries (in cents)
c = cost of one coke

COMMENTS

In order to solve the problem, positive whole multiples of 5 are needed to satisfy

$$
\begin{aligned}
h &> 2f & (1) \\
3f &> h+c & (2) \\
3c &> h & (3) \\
\text{and} \quad h+f+c &= 175 & (4)
\end{aligned}
$$

The hints are set up basically as a double loop: The outer loop, consisting of steps 2 through 12; increases f by fives from 5 to 165; and the inner loop, steps 3 through 9, increases h by fives from $5+2f$ to 165. Once values of f and h are chosen, c is calculated in step 3 in a way that guarantees equation (4) is satisfied. Since each of the values of f and h start at multiples of 5 and increase by fives and because of how c is calculated, all the values of f, h, and c created by the Hints are whole multiples of five. As step 2 starts h at $5+2f$ and the inner loop increases h by fives up to 165 while f is held constant, inequality (1) is guaranteed. The other necessary inequalities are checked in steps 4 and 5, and if these hold true, an answer is found. The loops end when h or f exceeds 165 because each of the three variables f, h, and c must be at least as large as 5 and their total cannot exceed 175.

113

ANSWERS AND EXTENSIONS

ANSWER: A hamburger costs $.95, order of French fries $.45, and a coke $.35.

```
0005 REM HAMBURGERS, FRENCH FRIES, AND A COKE
0010 LET F=5
0020 LET H=5+2*F
0030 LET C=175-F-H
0040 IF 3*F<=H+C THEN GOTO 0070
0050 IF 3*C<=H THEN GOTO 0070
0060 PRINT "HAMBURGERS COST ";H
0065 PRINT "FRENCH FRIES COST ";F;" AND"
0067 PRINT "A COKE COSTS ";C
0070 LET H=H+5
0080 IF H>165 THEN GOTO 0100
0090 GOTO 0030
0100 LET F=F+5
0110 IF F>165 THEN GOTO 0130
0120 GOTO 0020
0130 END
```

EXTENSION:

Prices inflate as time proceeds. The prices may have been 95¢, 45¢, and 35¢ when this book was written, but they may be considerably higher by the time you read it. Assume it is the year 2025 and prices are considerably higher. Indeed, assume that

$$
\begin{aligned}
h + f + c &= \$29.50 \\
h &> 3f \\
4f &> h + c \\
4c &> h
\end{aligned}
$$

and that all prices are multiples of 50¢. The Hints can locate the answer to this version of the problem if steps 1, 2, 3, 4, 5, 7, 8, 10, and 11 are changed to:

1. $f \leftarrow 50$
2. $h \leftarrow 50+3f$
3. $c \leftarrow 2{,}950-f-h$
4. Is $4f \leq h+c$? If yes, go to step 7.
5. Is $4c \leq h$? If yes, go to step 7.
7. $h \leftarrow h +50$
8. Is $h > 2{,}850$? If yes, go to step 10.
10. $f \leftarrow f + 50$
11. Is $f > 2850$? If yes, go to step 13.

THE LONGEST CHAIN

20

PROBLEM STATEMENT

There are 99 people at a party. Each is given one of the integers from 1 to 99 along with a set of instructions. The instructions say:

a. If your number is even, divide it by 2.
b. If your number odd, multiply by 3 and add 1.
c. Repeat these instructions on your new number until you arrive at the number 4.

Thus, each party-goer obtains a chain of integers ending with the number 4. For example, the party goer with the integer 3 produces the chain

$$3 \rightarrow 10 \rightarrow 5 \rightarrow 16 \rightarrow 8 \rightarrow 4$$

Which party-goer produces the longest chain?

HINTS

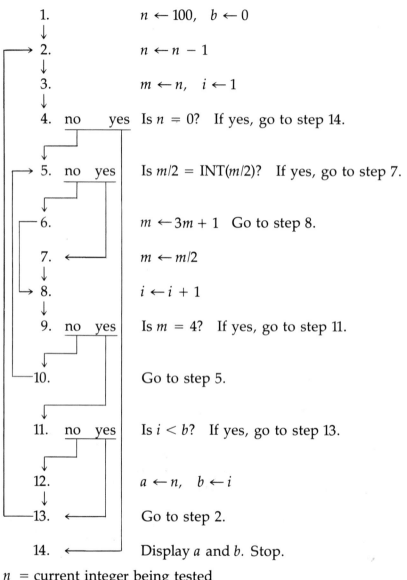

1. $n \leftarrow 100, \quad b \leftarrow 0$

2. $n \leftarrow n - 1$

3. $m \leftarrow n, \quad i \leftarrow 1$

4.   no   yes Is $n = 0$? If yes, go to step 14.

5.   no   yes Is $m/2 = \text{INT}(m/2)$? If yes, go to step 7.

6. $m \leftarrow 3m + 1$ Go to step 8.

7. $m \leftarrow m/2$

8. $i \leftarrow i + 1$

9.   no   yes Is $m = 4$? If yes, go to step 11.

10.   Go to step 5.

11. no   yes Is $i < b$? If yes, go to step 13.

12. $a \leftarrow n, \quad b \leftarrow i$

13.   Go to step 2.

14.   Display a and b. Stop.

n = current integer being tested
m = current sequence value in the chain
i = current chain length
a = integer with the longest chain
b = length of the longest chain

COMMENTS

The loop between steps 5 and 10 produces and counts the length of the chain for a given n value. The letter m represents each integer in the chain, and, when m becomes 4, the chain is completed. Then in step 11, the length i of this chain is compared to the length of the longest chain previously obtained. If longer—if "Is $i<b$?" has a "no" answer—the current n value and length of its chain are saved.

The loop between steps 2 and 13 starts n at 99 and decreases n by 1 during each loop until 0 is obtained. In this way the chains for all the integers between 99 and 1 are determined. When n becomes 0, the integer with the longest chain and the length of that longest chain are displayed.

ANSWERS AND EXTENSIONS

ANSWER: The party-goer with integer 97 produces the longest chain, a chain with 117 numbers.

```
0005 REM THE LONGEST CHAIN
0010 LET N=100
0015 LET B=0
0020 LET N=N-1
0030 LET M=N
0035 LET I=1
0040 IF N=0 THEN GOTO 0140
0050 IF M/2=INT(M/2) THEN GOTO 0070
0060 LET M=3*M+1
0065 GOTO 0080
0070 LET M=M/2
0080 LET I=I+1
0090 IF M=4 THEN GOTO 0110
0100 GOTO 0050
0110 IF I<B THEN GOTO 0130
0120 LET A=N
0125 LET B=I
0130 GOTO 0020
0140 PRINT "THE INTEGER WITH THE LONGEST CHAIN IS ";A
0145 PRINT "THE LENGTH OF THE LONGEST CHAIN IS ";B
0150 END
```

EXTENSION:

i. To find the integer that produces the longest chain for other intervals, say from 100 to 200, merely change steps 1 and 4 of the Hints to

1. $n \leftarrow 201$, $b \leftarrow 0$
4. Is $n = 99$? If yes, go to step 14.

In general, for the interval x to y, steps 2 and 4 are

1. $n \leftarrow y+1$, $b \leftarrow 0$
4. Is $n = x-1$? If yes, go to step 14.

Which integer in the range 100 to 200 has the longest chain?

ii. There are 14 integers from 1 to 99, other than 97, with chains of more than one hundred numbers. To find them change steps 11, 12, and 14. of the Hints to:

11. Is $i < 100$? If yes, go to step 13
12. $a \leftarrow n$, $b \leftarrow i$. Display a and b.
14. Stop.

SIX DIGIT DOOZIES

PROBLEM STATEMENT

a. Find the largest six-digit number that is both a perfect square and the product of two consecutive integers minus 400.

b. Find the largest six-digit number that is the product of two consecutive integers and that has the property that its left-most three digits form a number that is twice as large as the number formed from its right-most three digits.

c. Find the largest six-digit number that is both a triplet (that is, the left-most three digits are the same as the right-most three digits) and is also the product of two consecutive integers.

HINTS

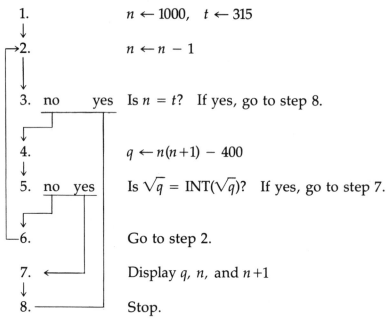

1. $\qquad$ $n \leftarrow 1000, \quad t \leftarrow 315$

2. $\qquad$ $n \leftarrow n - 1$

3. no $\quad$ yes $\quad$ Is $n = t$? If yes, go to step 8.

4. $\qquad$ $q \leftarrow n(n+1) - 400$

5. no $\quad$ yes $\quad$ Is $\sqrt{q} = \mathrm{INT}(\sqrt{q})$? If yes, go to step 7.

6. $\qquad$ Go to step 2.

7. $\leftarrow$ $\qquad$ Display q, n, and $n+1$

8. $\qquad$ Stop.

n = current integer being tested
t = smallest integer necessary to test
q = $n(n+1) - 400$

COMMENTS

a. The loop in steps 2 through 6 starts n at 1,000, decreases n by 1 during each loop, and ends when n is 315. These starting and ending values include all values of n for which $n(n+1)-400$ is a six-digit number. By looping from large n down to small n, the first solution is automatically the largest (six-digit) solution as well. The test "Is $\sqrt{q} = \text{INT}(\sqrt{q})$?" decides whether q is a perfect square. Note that round-off errors on your machine might require you to use these steps in place of step 5:

    5. $s \leftarrow \text{INT}(\sqrt{q} + .5)$
    5.5 Is $(s)(s) = q$? If yes, go to step 7.

b. To find the largest six-digit number that is both a perfect cube and the product of two consecutive integers plus 25, first notice that the range

$$315 \leqslant n \leqslant 999$$

still encompasses all n values for which $n(n+1)+25$ is a six-digit number. So step 1 does not need to be changed. Steps 4 and 5 do need to be changed, however;

    4. $q \leftarrow n(n+1)$, $r \leftarrow q/1000$
    5. Is $\text{INT}(r)/2 = 1,000\ \text{FRAC}(r)$? If yes, to to step 7.

You might need to use these steps in place of step 5:

    5. $s \leftarrow \text{INT}(1,000\ \text{FRAC}(r) + .5)$
    5.5 Is $\text{INT}(r)/2 = s$? If yes, go to step 7.

c. To find the largest six-digit number that is both a "triplet" and the product of two consecutive integers, merely change steps 4 and 5 to:

    4. $q \leftarrow n(n+1)$, $r \leftarrow q/1000$
    5. Is $\text{INT}(r)=1,000(\text{FRAC}(r))$? If yes, go to step 7.

Again, all values of n for which $n(n+1)$ is a six-digit number are included in

$$315 \leqslant n \leqslant 1000.$$

ANSWERS AND EXTENSIONS

ANSWERS:

a. The largest and only six-digit number that is both a perfect square and the product of two consecutive integers minus 400 is 160,000 = (400) (401) − 400 = 400².

b. The largest six-digit number that is the product of two consecutive integers and that has its left-most three digits equal to twice its right-most three digits, is 612,306 = (782) (783).

c. The largest six-digit number that is both a triplet and the product of two consecutive integers is 852,852 = (923) (924).

a.
```
0005 REM SIX DIGIT DOOZIES
0010 LET N=1000
0015 LET T=315
0020 LET N=N-1
0030 IF N=T THEN GOTO 0080
0040 LET Q=N*(N+1)-400
0050 IF SQR(Q)=INT(SQR(Q)) THEN GOTO 0070
0060 GOTO 0020
0070 PRINT " Q = ";Q;" N = ";N;" N+1 = ";N+1
0080 END
```

b.
```
0005 REM SIX DIGIT DOOZIES
0010 LET N=1000
0015 LET T=315
0020 LET N=N-1
0030 IF N=T THEN GOTO 0080
0040 LET Q=N*(N+1)
0045 LET R=Q/1000
0050 IF INT(R)/2=INT(1000*(R-INT(R))+.5) THEN GOTO 0070
0060 GOTO 0020
0070 PRINT " Q = ";Q;" N = ";N;" N+1 = ";N+1
0080 END
```

c.
```
0005 REM SIX DIGIT DOOZIES
0010 LET N=1000
0015 LET T=315
0020 LET N=N-1
0030 IF N=T THEN GOTO 0080
0040 LET Q=N*(N+1)
0045 LET R=Q/1000
```

```
0050 IF INT(R)=INT(1000*(R-INT(R))+.5) THEN GOTO 0070
0060 GOTO 0020
0070 PRINT " Q = ";Q;" N = ";N;" N+1 = ";N+1
0080 END
```

EXTENSIONS:

i. By changing step 7 in the Hints, you can find *all* six-digit numbers with the respective six-digit doozy properties. Use:

> 7. Display q, n, and $n+1$. Go to step 2.

ii. You can explore properties similar to those in this problem for eight-digit numbers by changing steps 1, 4, and 5. For example, to find the largest eight-digit number whose first four digits form the same number as the last four digits and that is the product of two consecutive integers, change steps 1, 4 and 5 to:

> 1. $n \leftarrow 3{,}162, \quad t \leftarrow 1{,}000$
> 4. $q \leftarrow n(n+1), \quad r \leftarrow q/10000$
> 6. Is $INT(r)=10{,}000(FRAC(r))$?
>   If yes, go to step 7.

THE AVERAGE LOOP

22

PROBLEM STATEMENT

Suppose you start with two numbers, specifically with $a = 100$ and $b = 200$ and follow these instructions:

a. Form the average of a and b, that is:

$$(a + b)/2$$

b. Replace a by b.
c. Replace b by the average

$$(a + b)/2$$

d. Repeat from step b.

After performing this activity many times, $(a + b)/2$ will tend to a limit. What value does this limit have?

HINTS

1.		$a \leftarrow 100, \quad b \leftarrow 200$
2.		$p \leftarrow b$
→3.		$c \leftarrow (a+b)/2$
4.	no yes	Is $c = p$? If yes, go to step 8.
5.		$a \leftarrow b$
6.		$b \leftarrow c, \quad p \leftarrow c$
7.		Go to step 3.
8.	←	Display c. Stop.

a = input first number
b = input second number
p = previous $(a+b)/2$
c = current $(a+b)/2$

COMMENTS

In the loop between steps 3 through 7, the appropriate instructions for the activity are performed. Specifically, instructions a, b, and c are accomplished in steps 3, 5, and 6 respectively.

The test in step 4 "Is $c = p$?" decides whether the newly calculated average equals the previous average or not. If so, a limit has been found, and the value of c is displayed. If not, the process is repeated.

Since programmable calculators and computers keep only a finite number of decimal places in the decimal expansion of any number, eventually the decimal values of c and p actually become equal. Therefore, a limit is found in a finite length of time.

ANSWERS AND EXTENSIONS

ANSWER: The average loop yields: a limiting average of 166.66666 (or perhaps 166.66667).

```
0005 REM THE AVERAGE LOOP
0010 LET A=100
0015 LET B=200
0020 LET P=B
0030 LET C=(A+B)/2
0040 IF C=P THEN GOTO 0080
0050 LET A=B
0060 LET B=C
0065 LET P=C
0070 GOTO 0030
0080 PRINT " AVE IS ";P
0090 END
```

EXTENSIONS:

i. For other input values, what limiting averages are produced? Try values of $a = 2$, $b = 5$; or $a = 0$, $b = 1$. For these variations, modify step 1 to become:

> 1. $a \leftarrow 2$, $b \leftarrow 5$
>
> or
>
> 1. $a \leftarrow 0$, $b \leftarrow 1$

What are the respective averages?

ii. By experimenting with various input values of a and b, you should eventually see a pattern from which you can guess the limiting average as a formula in terms of a and b. Can you guess this formula?

SAMANTHA'S FRACTION REDUCING MACHINE

PROBLEM STATEMENT

In order to take the drudgery out of checking student work on reducing fractions to simplest terms, teacher Samantha Smart turned her calculating device into a fraction-reducing machine.

For any fraction n/m Samantha could input n and m in that order and obtain the numerator and denominator, respectively, of the reduced fraction.

For the problem 30/27, Samantha inputed 30 and 27 and obtained 10 and 9, representing the answer 10/9 in simplest terms.

Create a program that duplicates Samantha's fraction-reducing machine.

HINTS

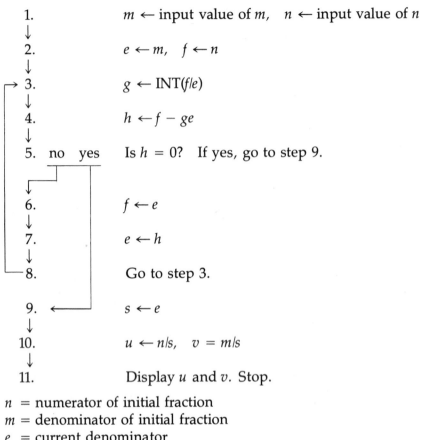

1. $m \leftarrow$ input value of m, $n \leftarrow$ input value of n

2. $e \leftarrow m,$ $f \leftarrow n$

3. $g \leftarrow \text{INT}(f/e)$

4. $h \leftarrow f - ge$

5. no yes   Is $h = 0$? If yes, go to step 9.

6. $f \leftarrow e$

7. $e \leftarrow h$

8.   Go to step 3.

9. $\leftarrow$ $s \leftarrow e$

10. $u \leftarrow n/s,$ $v = m/s$

11.   Display u and v. Stop.

n = numerator of initial fraction
m = denominator of initial fraction
e = current denominator
f = current numerator
g = current quotient
h = current remainder
s = greatest common divisor of n and m
u = numerator of the reduced fraction
v = denominator of the reduced fraction

COMMENTS

Steps 3 through 8 form a loop that locates the greatest common divisor of the input numbers n and m by the Euclidean Algorithm. When the test "Is $h = 0$?" has a "yes" answer, the algorithm terminates because the greatest common divisor has been found. This value is then stored in location s in step 9.

When the numerator n and denominator n of the original fraction are each divided by this greatest common divisor s the numerator u and denominator v of the reduced fraction are obtained (step 10). Since s is the largest integer that divides both n and m, the fraction u/v cannot be reduced any further and is therefore in its lowest terms.

In order to find the greatest common divisors in steps 3 through 8, f and e begin with the values of n and m. During each loop, f is divided by e and the results are placed in g and h, respectively (steps 3 and 4). If h is not yet zero, s has not yet been found, so steps 6 and 7 modify the values of f and e before looping back. Finally, after a finite length of time, h becomes zero, at which time e contains the greatest common divisor of n and m.

ANSWERS AND EXTENSIONS

ANSWER: No answer required.

```
0005 REM SAMANTHAS FRACTION REDUCING MACHINE
0010 PRINT "WHAT IS THE NUMERATOR";
0012 INPUT N
0015 PRINT "WHAT IS THE DENOMINATOR";
0017 INPUT M
0020 LET E=M
0025 LET F=N
0030 LET G=INT(F/E)
0040 LET H=F-G*E
0050 IF H=0 THEN GOTO 0090
0060 LET F=E
0070 LET E=H
0080 GOTO 0030
0090 LET S=E
0100 LET U=N/S
0105 LET V=M/S
0110 PRINT " THE FRACTION ";N;"/";M;" REDUCES TO ";U;"/";V
0120 END
```

EXTENSIONS:

i. Suppose Samantha wanted to adapt her fraction-reducing machine so that it would add two fractions *a/b* and *c/d* and then reduce the sum fraction to lowest terms. Can you adapt the Hints to accomplish this purpose? Change step 1, and add a step 0 as follows:

  0. $a \leftarrow$ input numerator of first fraction, $b \leftarrow$ input denominator of first fraction, $c \leftarrow$ input numerator of second fraction, $d \leftarrow$ input denominator of second fraction.
  1. $n \leftarrow ad + bc, \quad m = bd$

ii. The greatest common divisors of two positive numbers n and m is the largest integer that divides both n and m. The least common multiple of n and m is the smallest integer that is divisible by both n and m. Can you adapt the hints to turn the fraction-reducing machine into a greatest common divisor and least common multiple finder? Change steps 9 and 10 to:

  10. $l = nm/s$
  11. Display s and l. Stop.

THE KNOTTED ROPE

PROBLEM STATEMENT

A rope is knotted and joined at both ends so that it forms a loop with 90 equally spaced knots. In how many ways can it be stretched taut into a right triangle with knots at the corners of the triangle?

HINTS

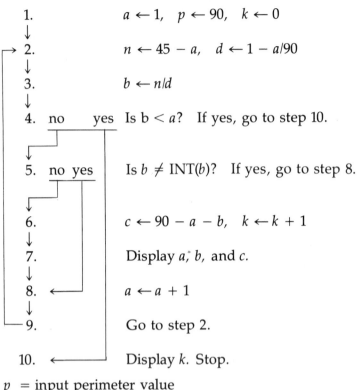

1. $a \leftarrow 1, \quad p \leftarrow 90, \quad k \leftarrow 0$

2. $n \leftarrow 45 - a, \quad d \leftarrow 1 - a/90$

3. $b \leftarrow n/d$

4. no   yes Is $b < a$?   If yes, go to step 10.

5. no yes   Is $b \neq \text{INT}(b)$?   If yes, go to step 8.

6. $c \leftarrow 90 - a - b, \quad k \leftarrow k + 1$

7.   Display $a,$ $b,$ and c.

8. $a \leftarrow a + 1$

9.   Go to step 2.

10.   Display k. Stop.

p = input perimeter value
a = smaller leg of the right triangle
b = larger leg of the right triangle
c = hypotenuse of the right triangle
n = numerator of b
d = denominator of b
k = number of possible right triangles

COMMENTS

If the two shorter legs are a and b, while the hypotenuse is c, these conditions must hold:

$a + b + c = 90$ (perimeter is 90)

$c^2 = a^2 + b^2$ (Pythagorean Theorem condition for right triangles)

Eliminating c gives

$$a^2 + b^2 = (90-a-b)^2$$

Now solving for b produces

$$b = (45-a)/(1-a/90)$$

So, for integer values of a, b can be calculated; and when b is also an integer, a solution is found.

It is only necessary to calculate b for values of a between 1 and 45, because for larger values of a, either b or c are necessarily negative. Within the range $1 \leqslant a \leqslant 45$, when a is small, b is large and when a is large, b is small. Therefore, it is not necessary to check further after the moment when b becomes less than a, because such checking would only locate solutions already found (with the roles of a and b reversed). Hence, a can always be thought of as the smaller leg of the right triangle. Values of b can be computed corresponding to integer values of a starting at $a = 1$ and ending when b becomes less than a for the first time.

Steps 2 through 9 of the Hints form a loop during which b is computed from an integer choice of a. If b is an integer, c is calculated, and a, b, and c are displayed (steps 5, 6, and 7). The loop starts the first time with $a = 1$ (step 1) and increases a by 1 during each loop (step 8). Once b becomes less than a (step 4), the looping can be concluded, as all possible right triangles will have been found. When each such triangle is found, 1 is added to a total k (step 6). After all possibilities have been checked—that is, once step 10 is reached—this total k is displayed.

ANSWERS AND EXTENSIONS

ANSWER: There are exactly two ways the rope may be stretched, namely, $(a,b,c)=(9,40,41)$ or $(15,36,39)$.

```
0005 REM THE KNOTTED ROPE
0010 LET A=1
0013 LET P=90
0017 LET K=0
0020 LET N=45-A
0025 LET D=1-A/90
0030 LET B=N/D
0040 IF B<A THEN GOTO 0100
0050 IF B<>INT(B) THEN GOTO 0080
0060 LET C=90-A-B
0065 LET K=K+1
0070 PRINT " SIDES ARE ";A;B;" AND ";C
0080 LET A=A+1
0090 GOTO 0020
0100 PRINT " TOTAL NUMBER OF POSSIBLE TRIANGLES IS ";K
0110 END
```

EXTENSIONS:

i. If the rope has 180 equally spaced knots, in how many ways can it be stretched taut to form a right triangle with knots at the corners? In order to obtain the three answers to this question, simply change steps 1, 2, and 6 of the Hints as follows:

     1. $a \leftarrow 1, \quad p \leftarrow 180, \quad k \leftarrow 0$
     2. $n \leftarrow 90\text{-}a, \quad d \leftarrow 1\text{-}a/180$
     6. $c \leftarrow 180\text{-}a\text{-}b, \quad k \leftarrow k + 1$

ii. For 360 equally spaced knots, there are four possible arrangements. Can you find them?

iii. While a permieter of 90 gives exactly two ways to stretch the rope, a perimeter of 12 gives only one, namely $(a,b,c)=(3,4,5)$. What is the smallest perimeter less than 90 that allows exactly two arrangements of the rope? To adapt the Hints, change steps 1, 2, 6, 7, and 10 and add steps 0, 11, 12, and 13:

     0. $p \leftarrow 2$
     1. $a \leftarrow 1, \quad k \leftarrow 0$
     2. $n \leftarrow (p/2)\text{-}a, \quad d \leftarrow 1\text{-}a/p$
     6. $c \leftarrow p\text{-}a\text{-}b, \quad k \leftarrow k+1$
     7. Display a, b, c, and p.
     10. $p \leftarrow p + 1$
     11. Is $p = 90$?   If yes, go to step 13
     12. Go to step 1.
     13. Stop.

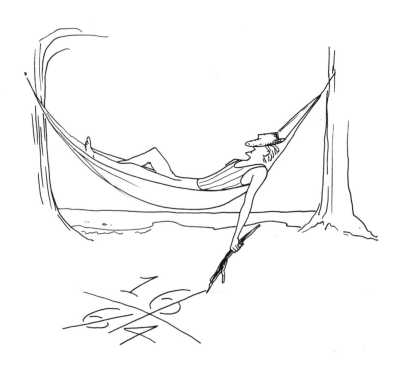

LAZY LENNY'S CANCELLATION

25

PROBLEM STATEMENT

When Lazy Lenny was asked to simplify the fraction 16/64, he simply cancelled the sixes. To his teacher's amazement, Lenny's cancellation technique produced a correct result:

$$\frac{1\!\!\!/6}{6\!\!\!/4} = \frac{1}{4}$$

What are all the fractions with two-digit numerators and denominators for which Lenny's technique gives an equal fraction?

HINTS

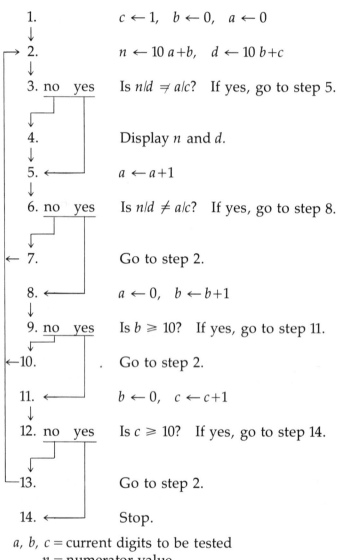

1. $c \leftarrow 1, \quad b \leftarrow 0, \quad a \leftarrow 0$

2. $n \leftarrow 10\,a + b, \quad d \leftarrow 10\,b + c$

3. no   yes   Is $n/d \neq a/c$?   If yes, go to step 5.

4. Display n and d.

5. $a \leftarrow a + 1$

6. no   yes   Is $n/d \neq a/c$?   If yes, go to step 8.

7. Go to step 2.

8. $a \leftarrow 0, \quad b \leftarrow b + 1$

9. no   yes   Is $b \geqslant 10$?   If yes, go to step 11.

10. Go to step 2.

11. $b \leftarrow 0, \quad c \leftarrow c + 1$

12. no   yes   Is $c \geqslant 10$?   If yes, go to step 14.

13. Go to step 2.

14. Stop.

$a, b, c =$ current digits to be tested
$n =$ numerator value
$d =$ denominator value

COMMENTS

In order for a cancellation to be possible, the fraction must be of the form

$$\frac{ab}{bc} = \frac{a}{c}$$

Expressed in more mathematical terms, the fraction on the left equals the fraction on the right only when

$$(10a + b)/(10b + c) = a/c$$

Step 2 of the Hints forms the numerator n and the denominator d of the fraction $(10a + b)/(10b + c)$. Then step 3 tests whether the fractions n/d and a/c are equal. If they are equal, the numerator and denominator, n and d, are displayed to show a solution.

The three nested loops in steps 2 through 7, 2 through 10, and 2 through 13 create all combinations of a, b, and c with $0 \leq a \leq 9$, $0 \leq b \leq 9$, and $1 \leq c, \leq 9$. The cases with $c = 0$ are excluded so that division by zero never occurs.

ANSWERS AND EXTENSIONS

ANSWER: There are nine solutions, each with repetitions of one of the digits 1, 2, . . ., or 9. For example,

$$\frac{2\not{2}}{\not{2}2} = \frac{2}{2}$$

Furthermore, there are four other fractions, namely

$$\frac{4\not{9}}{\not{9}8} = \frac{4}{8}, \quad \frac{1\not{6}}{\not{6}4} = \frac{1}{4}, \quad \frac{2\not{6}}{\not{6}5} = \frac{2}{5}, \quad \frac{1\not{9}}{\not{9}5} = \frac{1}{5}$$

```
0005 REM LAZY LENNY'S CANCELLATIONS
0010 LET C=1
0013 LET B=0
0017 LET A=0
0020 LET N=10*A+B
0025 LET D=10*B+C
0030 IF N/D<>A/C THEN GOTO 0050
0040 PRINT " FRACTION IS ";N;"/";D
0050 LET A=A+1
0060 IF A>=10 THEN GOTO 0080
0070 GOTO 0020
0080 LET A=0
0085 LET B=B+1
0090 IF B>=10 THEN GOTO 0110
0100 GOTO 0020
0110 LET B=0
0115 LET C=C+1
0120 IF C>=10 THEN GOTO 0140
0130 GOTO 0020
0140 END
```

EXTENSIONS:

i. If Lenny were to cancel the other two digits, he would obtain

$$\frac{ab}{ca} = \frac{b}{c}$$

or, more mathematically, fractions $n/d = b/c$, where $n = 10a+b$ and $d = 10c+a$. What fractions have this cancellation property? To locate these fractions, change steps 2 and 3:

   2. $n \leftarrow 10a+b, \quad d \leftarrow 10c+a$
   3. Is $n/d \neq b/c$? If yes, go to step 5.

ii. Lenny might be inclined to make other illegal computations. Suppose he tried computing

$$a^b + c^b \quad \text{as} \quad ab + cb$$

Can you find all solutions for digits a, b, and c for which these different operations produce the same result? Change steps 1, 2, 3, and 4 to:

   1. $c \leftarrow 0, \quad b \leftarrow 0, \quad a \leftarrow 0$
   2. $x \leftarrow a^b + c^b, \quad y \leftarrow ab + cb$
   3. Is $x \neq y$? If yes, go to step 5.
   4. Display $(a^b + c^b)$ and $(ab + cb)$.

THE MIDDLE OF
THE SQUARE

26

PROBLEM STATEMENT

An early procedure for generating random numbers, proposed by John von Neumann, was the "middle of the square" method. Starting with a four-digit integer, the middle four digits of the square of that integer are then chosen as the next integer. Then the process is repeated. For example, if the starting number 1,234 is chosen,

$$1,234 \rightarrow (1,234)^2 = \ \ 1,552,756 \rightarrow 5,227$$
$$5,227 \rightarrow (5,227)^2 = 27,321,529 \rightarrow 3,215$$
$$3,215 \rightarrow (3,215)^2 = 10,336,225 \rightarrow 3,362$$
$$3,362 \rightarrow \text{etc.}$$

However, this method is not successful because it tends to produce short sequences that repeat. In fact some four-digit numbers were found that have themselves as the middle part of their squares. Each produces a sequence of repetitions of the same four-digit number and is certainly not random.

Can you find those numbers?

HINTS

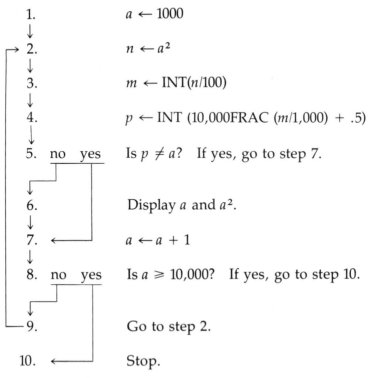

1. $a \leftarrow 1000$

2. $n \leftarrow a^2$

3. $m \leftarrow \text{INT}(n/100)$

4. $p \leftarrow \text{INT}\ (10{,}000\text{FRAC}\ (m/1{,}000) + .5)$

5. no yes   Is $p \neq a$?   If yes, go to step 7.

6.   Display a and a^2.

7. $a \leftarrow a + 1$

8. no yes   Is $a \geqslant 10{,}000$?   If yes, go to step 10.

9.   Go to step 2.

10.   Stop.

a = current four-digit number
n = square of a
m = all but the two right-most digits of n
p = middle four digits of n

COMMENTS

Steps 2 through 9 form a loop that starts a at 1,000, increases a by 1 during each loop, and ends when a becomes a five-digit number. During each loop, a^2 is computed in step 2, and the middle four digits of a^2 are obtained in steps 3 and 4 by removing the first two digits on the right and choosing the next four digits. The test "Is $p \neq a$?" decides whether a is the middle four digits of its square, and step 6 displays only those values of a that have this property.

When "Is $a \geq 10,000$?" has a "yes" answer, all the four-digit possibilities for a have been tested, so the looping terminates.

ANSWERS AND EXTENSIONS

ANSWER: There are three four-digit numbers that have themselves as the middle part of their squares. They are:

$$2{,}500^2 = 6{,}250{,}000$$
$$3{,}792^2 = 14{,}379{,}264$$
$$7{,}600^2 = 57{,}760{,}000$$

```
0005 REM MIDDLE OF THE SQUARE PROBLEM
0010 LET A=1000
0020 LET N=A*A
0030 LET M=INT(N/100)
0040 LET P=INT(10000*(M/10000-INT(M/10000))+.5)
0050 IF P<>A THEN GOTO 0070
0060 PRINT " SAME MIDDLE FOR ";A;" NOTE ";A*A
0070 LET A=A+1
0080 IF A>=10000 THEN GOTO 0100
0090 GOTO 0020
0100 END
```

EXTENSIONS:

i. Do any three-digit numbers have squares whose "middle" three digits in the tens, hundreds, and thousands places are the original three-digit number? To answer this question, adapt the Hints by changing steps 1, 3, 4, and 8:

> 1. $a \leftarrow 100$
> 3. $m \leftarrow \text{INT}(n/10)$
> 4. $p \leftarrow \text{INT}(1{,}000\text{FRAC}(m/1{,}000) + .5)$
> 8. Is $a \geq 1{,}000$? If yes, go to step 10.

ii. Does the product of any four-digit number a with one more than that number, $a + 1$, have the sum, $2a + 1$, of those two consecutive numbers as the middle four digits of the product? Change steps 2, 5, and 6 of the Hints to:

> 2. $n \leftarrow a\,(a + 1)$
> 5. Is $p \neq 2a + 1$? If yes, go to step 7.
> 6. Display a, $a + 1$, and $a\,(a + 1)$.

iii. Does the product of any three-digit number a with one more than that number, $a + 1$, have their sum, $2a + 1$, as the "middle" three digits? Change steps 1, 2, 3, 4, 5, 6, and 8 to:

> 1. $a \leftarrow 100$
> 2. $n \leftarrow a(a + 1)$
> 3. $m \leftarrow \text{INT}(n/10)$
> 4. $p \leftarrow \text{INT}(1{,}000\text{FRAC}(m/1{,}000) + .5)$
> 5. Is $p \neq 2a + 1$? If yes, go to step 7.
> 6. Display a, $a + 1$, and $a(a + 1)$.
> 8. Is $a \geq 1{,}000$? If yes, go to step 10.

ANSWER KEY FOR THE EXTENSIONS OF THE PROBLEMS

0. Sal's Vases extensions:
   i.   Sal must have had 55 vases left to sell.
   ii.   Either 42, 98, or 154.

1. Pyramid of Cannonballs extensions:
   i.   42,925 cannonballs are required to make 50 layers.
   ii.   24 layers use 4,900 cannonballs.
   iii. Either 1 layer with 1 cannonball or 2 layers with 9 cannonballs.

2. Narcissistic Cubes extensions:
   i.   Narcissistic squares: just 0 and 1
         Narcissistic fourth-powers: just 0 and 1.
   ii.   8,833

3. Prisoner's Dilemma extensions:
   i.   For 15 marbles, the probability is 0.741379 with one green marble and no red marbles in one of the urns.
   ii. For 20, 30, and 100 marbles, the best probability again occurs with one green marble and no red marbles in one of the urns; the respective best probabilities are 0.743590, 0.745763, and 0.748744. Note that as the number of marbles increases, the best probability approaches 75%.

4. The Malfunctioning Clock extensions:
   i.   The clock loses 1.99993 minutes in 48 hours and 2.00000 minutes in 72 hours.
   ii. It takes 65 hours for the number of minutes lost to appear to be exactly 2 minutes when rounded off to six significant digits.
   iii. 0.6 minutes lost in 24 hours.

5. The Efficiency Expert extensions:
   i. $x = 172$ with $y = 379$ or $x = 392$ with $y = 146$.

6. The Pervasive Roots extensions:
   i.   For $n = 2$ the pervasive square root is 2,
        for $n = 6$ the pervasive square root is 3,
        for $n = 12$, the pervasive root is 4,
        for $n = 20$, the root is 5,
        in general, for $n = a(a-1)$, the pervasive square root is a $(a \geqslant 2)$.
   ii. For $n = 6$ the pervasive cube root is 2,
        for $n = 24$ the pervasive cube root is 3,
        for $n = 60$ the pervasive root is 4,
        for $n = 120$ the root is 5,
        for $n = 210$ the root is 6,
        in general, for $n = (a+1)(a)(a-1)$, the pervasive fourth root is a $(a \geqslant 2)$.
        For $n = 14$ the pervasive fourth root is 2,
        for $n = 78$ the pervasive fourth root is 3,
        for $n = 252$ the pervasive root is 4,
        and for $n = 620$, the pervasive fourth root is 5.

7. The Game of 100 extensions: Winning strategy: First choose 6 to make the first total equal to 7. Then for whatever the machine chooses during its turn, you choose 9 minus the machine's choice.

8. The Politicians Banquet extensions:
   i.   12 senators, 86 congressmen, and 2 guests.
   ii. Either 30 senators, 70 congressmen, and 100 guests, or 89 senators, 35 congressmen, and 76 guests.
   iii. 12 senators, 34 congressmen, and 56 guests.
9. The Supported Ladder extensions: 3.4, 1.2, −2.5
10. The Postage Stamp Problem extensions:
    i.   407
    ii. 29¢
    iii. The largest number not attainable from (non-negative) combinations of a and b is the number given by the formula: $ab - (a+b)$.
11. Persistence Number extensions:
    i.   No answer required.
    ii. 25 is the smallest with persistence number 2,
         39 is the smallest with persistence number 3,
         77 is the smallest with persistence 4,
         679 is the smallest with persistence 5.
    iii. No answer required.
12. High-Low Game extensions:
    i.   No answer required.
    ii. Starting with the range of possible values of 0 to 99, first make a guess of 50. If you see a huge number, your guess was too high, so make a next guess that is halfway between 0 and 50, namely 25. If, on the other hand, you see a small number, your guess was too low, so guess halfway between 50 and 99, namely, 75. After each guess, you will see either your guess, if the guess was right; a huge number, if your guess was too high; or a small number, if your guess was too low. By guessing in the middle of the remaining range of possibilities, you can cut the list of possible values in half after each guess. With this strategy you can guess the correct answer, for numbers between 0 and 99, in 7 or fewer guesses.
13. The Football Jerseys extensions:
    i.   No
    ii. $(4(57-76))^2 = 5{,}776$.
    iii. $(494 + 209)^2 = 494{,}209$ and $(998 + 001)^2 = 998{,}001$.

14. Intriguing Integers extensions:
    i.   28, 29, 30
    ii. 12, 13, 14, 15
15. Finding Unit Fractions extensions:
    i. $1/6 = 1/7 + 1/42 = 1/8 + 1/24 = 1/9 + 1/18 = 1/10 + 1/15 = 1/12 + 1/12.$
    ii. 8/256
    iii. $5/360 = 1/144 + 1/144$ with smallest product of denominators. In fact, the smallest product of denominators always corresponds to the case where the denominators are closest together.
16. The Time of Day extensions: No others.
17. How Big Is the Fleet extensions:
    i.   One additional truck, numbered 625.
    ii. Now 18 trucks are possible, numbered 1, 4, 5, 6, 9, 24, 25, 49, 51, 75, 76, 99, 125, 249, 251, 375, 376, and 499. If numbers up to 1,000 are permitted, seven additional trucks can be added with numbers 501, 624, 625, 749, 751, 875, and 999.
18. The Fowl Problem extensions: Either 2 roosters, 9 hens, and 189 chicks or 6 roosters, 2 hens, and 192 chicks.
19. Hamburgers, French Fries, and a Coke extensions: Hamburgers cost $18.50, french fries cost $6.00 and a coke costs $5.00.
20. The Longest Chain Extensions:
    i. $n = 171$ has chain length 123.
    ii. They are 95, 94, 83, 82, 73, 71, 63, 62, 55, 54, 47, 41, 31, and 27.
21. Six-Digit Doozies extensions:
    i.   a. No others.
         b. $444,222 = (666)(667)$ and $304,152 = (551)(552)$.
         c. $510,510 = (714)(715)$ and $406,406 = (637)(638)$ and $132,132 = (363)(364)$.
    ii. Only $01,200,120 = (1095)(1096)$.
22. The Average Loop Extensions:
    i.   4 and 0.666667, respectively.
    ii. $(a + 2b)/3$
23. Samantha's Fraction-Reducing Machine extensions:
    i.   No answer required.
    ii. No answer required.

24. The Knotted Rope extensions:
    i.   (18, 80, 82),   (30, 72, 78),   and   (45, 60, 75).
    ii. (36, 160, 164), (60, 144, 156), (72, 135, 153), and (90, 120, 150).
    iii. Perimeter is 60.
25. Lazy Lenny's Cancellations extensions:
    i.   Essentially the same fractions as in the original problem, but upside down.
    ii. Obvious answers occur for $b = 1$, like $4 = 3^1 + 1^1 = (3)(1) + (1)(1)$ and for $a = c = 0$, like $0 = 0^3 + 0^3 = (0)(3) + (0)(3)$; non-obvious answers are: $9 = 2^3 + 1^3 = (2)(3) + (1)(3)$, $8 = 2^2 + 2^2 + (2)(2) + (2)(2)$, and $4 = 2^2 + 0^2 = (2)(2) + (0)(2)$.
26. Middle of the Square extensions:
    i.   250 and 760.
    ii. $(2102)(2103) = 4,420,506$
    iii. $(110)(111) = 12,210$ and $(183)(184) = 33,672$.